Skills Practice

Annotated Teacher's Edition

**Level 4
Book 2**

McGraw Hill | SRA

Columbus, OH

SRAonline.com

Send all inquiries to this address:
SRA/McGraw-Hill
4400 Easton Commons
Columbus, OH 43219-6188

ISBN: 978-0-07-610495-6
MHID: 0-07-610495-8

2 3 4 5 6 7 8 9 QPD 13 12 11 10 09 08

The McGraw·Hill Companies

Table of Contents

Unit 4 Science Fair

Unit 5 America on the Move

6 Unit Dollars and Sense

Name _____ Date _____

Root Plus Suffix *-ic*, *-ly*, *-ist*, *-er*

Focus

A **suffix** is an addition to the end of a word. Example: call*ing*

A **root word** is a word to which a suffix can be added. Example: *call*ing

Adding the **suffix -ly** to the end of words changes adjectives to adverbs, which describe the way something occurs. Example: *happily*

The **suffix -ly** also changes root words that are nouns into adjectives. Example: *fatherly*

The **suffix -ic** means "having to do with." The root word changes from a noun to an adjective when this suffix is added. Example: *scientific*

The **suffix -ist** means "one who practices." In this case, the part of speech of the root word does not change. Example: *scientist*

The **suffix -er** changes verbs to nouns. Example: *farmer*

Practice A Add either the suffix *-ic* or *-ly* to make a new word.

1. sister ___sisterly___

2. hieroglyph ___hieroglyphic___

3. magnet ___magnetic___

4. quick ___quickly___

5. complete ___completely___

6. prophet ___prophetic___

Practice B   Add either the suffix *-ist* or *-er* to make a new word. Remember that when adding the suffix *-ist*, the final letter of the root word is often dropped.

7. dream   dreamer

8. biology   biologist

9. pharmacy   pharmacist

10. paint   painter

11. sell   seller

12. piano   pianist

13. train   trainer

14. play   player

Apply   Add a suffix to each word *(-ic, -ly, -ist, or -er)* to make it the part of speech written in parentheses. Then write each new word in a sentence.   **Possible Answers**

15. teach (noun) My teacher is one of the nicest people I know.

16. sudden (adverb) She slammed on her brakes suddenly to avoid hitting the cat.

17. geology (noun) Jeff loves rocks and dreams of becoming a geologist.

18. volcano (adjective) This mountain is made of volcanic ash.

Name _____ Date _____

Selection Vocabulary

Focus

crabbier (kra' • bē • ûr) *adj.* form of **crabby:** cross; in a bad mood (page 355)

local (lō' • kəl) *adj.* nearby (page 356)

observations (ob' • sûr • vā' • shənz) *n.* plural of **observation:** an act of noticing something (page 358)

examine (ik • za' • mən) *v.* to look closely (page 359)

certain (sûr' • tən) *adj.* sure (page 363)

react (rē • akt') *v.* to act because something has happened (page 363)

results (ri • zults') *n.* plural of **result:** what you find out when you do an experiment (page 362)

anxious (angk' • shəs) *adj.* eager (page 366)

Practice   **Write the vocabulary word that best matches the underlined word or phrase in the sentences below.**

1. You might want to <u>inspect</u> the carton of eggs to see if any

are cracked. _____ examine _____

2. Trevor didn't <u>respond</u> to his father's news very well.

_____ react _____

3. Ashley was <u>concerned</u> about the trip.

_____ anxious _____

4. We must remember to record the <u>findings</u> of our science

experiment. _____ results _____

5. Molly's little sister is <u>more irritated</u> when she doesn't take

an afternoon nap. _____ crabbier _____

Apply Fill in the blank with a vocabulary word from this lesson to complete each sentence.

6. I thought you would feel better after a good night's sleep, but you seem _____ crabbier _____.

7. Are you _____ certain _____ that the show starts at 8:00?

8. If you want the bully to leave you alone, don't _____ react _____ to his teasing.

9. Kiyama and I didn't get the _____ results _____ we expected when we conducted our survey.

10. Ben ran down to the _____ local _____ candy store to buy a gift for his grandparents.

11. The doctor will carefully _____ examine _____ you during your annual check-up.

12. I like to watch people in the mall and make _____ observations _____ about them.

13. Tanner is _____ anxious _____ to get the race started.

Name _____ Date _____

Parts of a Library

Libraries are an important part of your research process. Libraries are full of resources to help you find just about any kind of information you can imagine.

- The reference section contains almanacs, dictionaries, atlases, and encyclopedias.
- Periodicals include magazines and newspapers.
- Fiction books are organized by the author's last name, nonfiction books by subject matter.
- Many libraries provide electronic resources, including periodical databases, reference software, and the Internet.
- Most libraries have card catalogs available electronically, allowing you to search material by title, author, or subject.

Which sections of the library have you used in the past?

Possible Answer the reference section, the fiction section

Which section of the library is your favorite, and why?

Possible Answer I like the fiction section, because I like to read stories.

Which section have you found most helpful when doing research? What helpful resources have you found there?

Possible Answer When I was researching current events in the Middle East, I found a lot of good magazine articles in the periodical section.

Visit a local library and find the following resources. Write the title of the resource on the line provided.

1. A fiction book by a favorite author

Possible Answer *Harry Potter and the Goblet of Fire*

2. A book about science fair projects

Possible Answer *Sure-to-Win Science Fair Projects*

3. A magazine about sports

Possible Answer "Sports Illustrated for Kids"

4. An encyclopedia article about dogs

Possible Answer "Dogs"

5. A newspaper article about an event in your city or town

Possible Answer "Local Girl Saves Dog"

Choose a topic related to the scientific method. While at the library, make a list of sources you could use to help you research your topic.

Possible Answers Topic: How Magnets Work; Sources: encyclopedia, non-fiction books, the Internet

Name _____ Date _____

Writing a Summary

Think

Audience: Who will read your summary?

Possible Answers My classmates and teacher

Purpose: What is your reason for writing a summary?

Possible Answer I want to tell them what a story is about without them having to read the whole thing.

Prewriting

Use this graphic organizer to summarize a story of your choice. Write the main idea and details of the story. **Possible Answers**

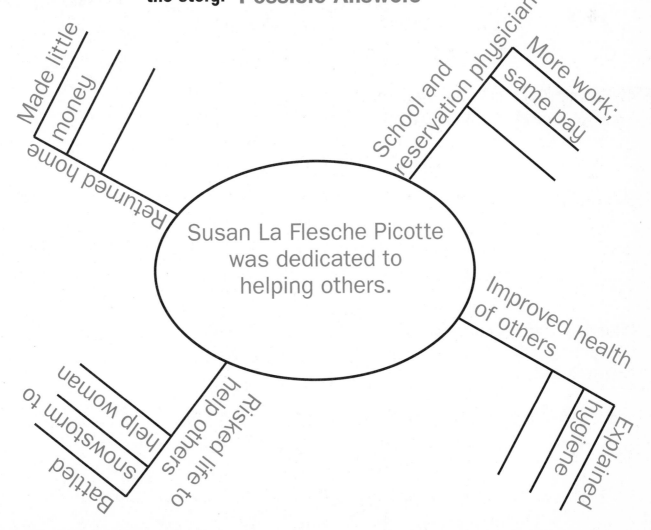

Revising

Use this checklist to revise your summary.

☐ Do you write about the main idea of the selection?

☐ Do you include only the most important details?

☐ Do the other sentences in the paragraph support the main idea?

Editing/Proofreading

Use this checklist to correct mistakes in your summary.

☐ Did you check your spelling?

☐ Are commas and other punctuation used correctly?

☐ Are pronouns used correctly? Do they agree with their antecedents in number and gender?

Publishing

Use this checklist to get ready for publication.

☐ Read your summary again to make sure it is complete.

☐ Write or type a neat final copy.

Name _____ Date _____

Root word plus suffix

Focus
- When suffixes are added to root words, the meaning of the root word changes.
- *–ity* changes an adjective into a noun
- *–al* changes a noun into an adjective
- *–less* means without
- *–or* means a person with _____
- *–ly* means in a _____ way

Practice **Write the spelling words made from these root words.**

-ity, changes an adjective into a noun

1. local ___locality___   3. odd ___oddity___

2. humid ___humidity___

-less, without

4. price ___priceless___   6. life ___lifeless___

5. flavor ___flavorless___

-or, a person who does something

7. act ___actor___   9. inspect ___inspector___

8. collect ___collector___

-al, changes a noun into an adjective

10. norm ___normal___   12. nation ___national___

11. critic ___critical___

Word List
1. locality
2. oddity
3. humidity
4. finality
5. priceless
6. flavorless
7. needless
8. lifeless
9. actor
10. editor
11. collector
12. inspector
13. normal
14. digital
15. critical
16. national
17. briskly
18. jointly
19. properly
20. vividly

Challenge Words
21. governor
22. certainly
23. entirely

-ly, in a certain way

13. brisk <u>briskly</u>   **15.** proper <u>properly</u>

14. joint <u>jointly</u>

Apply   Write the spelling word you can make with each group of letters.

16. anifiytl <u>finality</u>

17. dvliviy <u>vividly</u>

18. loolccetr <u>collector</u>

19. tacro <u>actor</u>

20. clepssrie <u>priceless</u>

Add the suffixes –or, -al, -ly, or –ity to write a spelling word. The first one is done for you.

	-or	-al	-ly	-ity	
21. inspect	___	___	___	___	inspector
22. nation	___	___	___	___	national
23. odd	___	___	___	___	oddity
24. brisk	___	___	___	___	briskly

Challenge

| **25.** certain | ___ | ___ | ___ | ___ | certainly |
| **26.** govern | ___ | ___ | ___ | ___ | governor |

Name _____ Date _____

Regular Verbs

Focus

Regular verbs are verbs that follow a certain pattern when they change tenses.

Laugh is a **regular verb.**

They *laugh.* She *laughed.*

Laugh and *laughed* are forms of the verb *to laugh. Laugh* shows an action currently happening, while *laughed* shows an action in the past.

If the subject of a sentence is singular, most verbs add *-s* or *-es* to create the present tense, but add nothing for plural subjects.

To form the past tense, add *-ed* to the verb.

Practice A

Change each of these regular verbs to the past tense.

1. gallop ___galloped___
2. play ___played___
3. follow ___followed___
4. smile ___smiled___

Change each of these regular verbs to the present tense.

5. expected ___expect___
6. pulled ___pull___
7. crawled ___crawl___
8. rowed ___row___

Practice B Circle the correct form of the verb in parentheses.

9. My baby sister (grab/**grabs**) everything in sight.

10. Kia and Sienna (pick/**picked**) cherries yesterday morning.

11. Last week, my brother (want/**wanted**) to go skiing, but now he doesn't.

12. My horses (**roll**/rolls) on their backs in the grass.

13. We (**cheer**/cheers) loudly at every football game.

14. Deston likes to (**climb**/climbed) on the jungle gym.

15. The farmer (ask/**asked**) his horse if he wanted some hay.

Apply Rewrite each sentence changing the underlined verbs to the present tense. You may have to change some of the other words in the sentence for it to make sense.

16. My dogs <u>barked</u> all night last night. **Possible Answer** My dogs bark all night some nights.

17. Leeza <u>tied</u> a knot in the rope. **Possible Answer** Leeza ties a knot in the rope.

18. Alec and Heni <u>reminded</u> the teacher to collect the homework. **Possible Answer** Alec and Heni remind the teacher to collect the homework.

Name _____ **Date** _____

Roots plus prefixes *mis-*, *un-*, *dis-*, and *im-*

Focus

The **prefixes mis-, un-, dis-** and **im-** all have a similar meaning: *not*, or *opposite*.

Examples: *mis*fortune, *un*happy, *dis*agree, *im*possible

Practice A Add the correct prefix (*mis-, un-, dis-,* or *im-*) to each word to give it the opposite meaning. You may use a dictionary if needed.

1. judge   misjudge
2. screw   unscrew
3. honest   dishonest
4. conduct   misconduct
5. infect   disinfect
6. patient   impatient
7. behave   misbehave
8. perfect   imperfect
9. pack   unpack
10. steady   unsteady

Practice B
Match each definition below with a word from the word box.

dislike	distrust	impolite	misplace	unnatural	unprepared

11. not have faith in _____ distrust _____

12. not normal _____ unnatural _____

13. not be fond of _____ dislike _____

14. put in the wrong spot _____ misplace _____

15. not very nice _____ impolite _____

16. not ready _____ unprepared _____

Apply
Write a definition of each word based on the meaning of the prefix and the root word. You may not use the root word in your definition.

17. unskilled __**Possible Answer** not good at something__

18. mispronounce **Possible Answer** to say something wrong

19. disappear __**Possible Answer** to not be visible anymore__

20. untidy __**Possible Answer** not neat__

21. imperfect __**Possible Answer** not flawless__

22. unpopular __**Possible Answer** not well-liked__

Name _____ Date _____

Selection Vocabulary

Practice   **Write the word that best fits each clue below.**

1. If two people are in the same family, what do we say

   they are? _____ related _____

2. What does a flower do to a bee? _____ attract _____

3. If the water is clean and clear and has no chemicals in it,

   what is it? _____ pure _____

4. What do we call a stream of electricity? _____ current _____

5. What is the very middle of the earth is called?

   _____ core _____

6. What are you measuring when you see how

   hard something is pushing something else? _____ force _____

Apply Write the vocabulary word next to the group of words that have a similar meaning.

7. energy; intensity; vigor   _____force_____

8. hardly; infrequently; occasionally   _____rarely_____

9. moving; rubbing; scraping   _____friction_____

10. clean; uncontaminated; untainted   _____pure_____

11. associated; connected; aligned   _____related_____

12. stream; flow; line   _____current_____

13. pull; fascinate; bring together   _____attract_____

14. inside; middle; depths   _____core_____

Name _____ Date _____

Evaluating Questions for Investigation

When choosing a question to investigate, it is important to select a question that is neither too narrow nor too broad. On the next page, you will learn some strategies for evaluating questions.

Think of a question you have investigated in the past. Write it here.

Possible Answer Why do people get headaches?

_____

Was the question too narrow, too broad, or just right? How did you decide this?

Possible Answer It was just right. I began checking sources, and I found enough information, but it wasn't overwhelming.

The selections in this unit contain many possibilities for investigation. Scan the selections and see how you could further investigate the concept of the scientific method. Write some questions you would like to investigate further.

Possible Answers How do birds know to fly south for the winter? How does our brain work? What is life like at the North Pole? How do sailboats work? Why do people get headaches?

_____

Evaluation Strategies

- Conduct a search using keywords. If few or no sources are available, the question may be too narrow. If hundreds of sources are available, the question may be too broad.

- Break the question into as many subtopics as you can brainstorm. If you have more than five, your question is probably too broad. If you have only one or two subtopics, then your question is most likely too narrow.

On the bottom of the previous page, you made a list of possible questions. Choose one of them to evaluate.

Possible Answer What is life like at the North Pole?

First, conduct a search on keywords related to your question. You may use the Internet or the library. How many sources did you find? Is this enough/not enough/too many? Why do you think so?

Possible Answer I found hundreds of sources. This is too many. I need to narrow my search.

Divide your topic into as many subtopics as you can brainstorm. Write those subtopics here.

Possible Answers penguins, polar bears, glaciers, ice fishing, arctic terns, narwhals

Based on your evaluation, is your question too broad, too narrow, or just right? If you need to revise your question, write your new question here.

Possible Answer What is life like for the migrating arctic tern?

Organizing Expository Writing

Focus

When you write to give information or to explain something, you must organize the information for your readers. The method of organization usually depends on the type of information you are providing your readers. Three common methods are **compare and contrast, cause and effect,** and **question and answer.**

- You can **compare and contrast** two things to point out how they are alike and how they are different. This method works well for comparing two products, two characters in a book or movie, or two animals, for example.

- You can explore **cause-and-effect relationships.** Historians and scientists often use this method of organization. You might explain events that caused another larger event. You might explain what causes northern lights to appear in the sky.

- You can use a **question-and-answer approach.** Begin by asking a question. Then give the answer by explaining the process or providing background for the readers.

Practice

For each topic, tell whether the writer should organize the writing using compare and contrast, cause and effect, or question and answer.

1. elementary school and middle school

   _compare and contrast_____

2. the benefits of participating in team athletic activities

   _cause and effect *or* question and answer_____

3. the impact of watching television after school

   _cause and effect_____

UNIT 4 Lesson 2

Apply Read each expository paragraph. After each paragraph, tell what method of organization the writer uses—compare and contrast, cause and effect, or question and answer.

4. Have you ever been tricked by nature? Some plants and animals are *supposed* to be tricky. For example, the walking stick looks like a stick so it doesn't get eaten. Chameleons change colors to fool their enemies, and some butterflies' wings have markings that look like owls. The markings scare away birds that might want to eat the butterfly.

question and answer

5. The team's old So-Hi shoes had great support. They were also sturdy and they lasted the whole season. Everyone on the team was satisfied with them. This season, the team is wearing Troopers. There have been two foot injuries already, and two players have had to replace shoes whose soles were damaged. Team members agree that So-Hi shoes seem to be of better quality than Troopers.

compare and contrast

What after-school activities take place at your school? Are there athletic teams, art classes, or reading clubs available? Write a paragraph about one or several of these activities. Use compare and contrast, cause and effect, or question and answer to organize your paragraph.

Possible Answer Are you a creative person who likes to paint, draw, build, or sculpt? Do you wish you had a place to express your creativity? If so, after-school art classes are for you! Each week, there are new skills to learn and new projects to create. You'll paint pictures, draw portraits, make collages, sculpt figurines out of clay, and much more. Your artwork will be displayed around the school for others to enjoy and admire. It will require a lot of hard work, but the results will be worth it!

Name _____ Date _____

Root words plus prefix

Focus
- When prefixes are added to root words, the meaning of the root word changes.
  - *de-* means take away, or do the opposite
  - *im-* means not
  - *pre-* means before
  - *co-* means together, with
  - *en-* means to cause to be _____

Practice Write the spelling words made from these root words.

de-, to take away or do the opposite

1. claw ___declaw___   2. rail ___derail___

im-, not

3. polite ___impolite___   5. perfect ___imperfect___

4. mobile ___immobile___

pre, before

6. view ___preview___   8. school ___preschool___

7. heat ___preheat___

en-, to cause to be _____

9. force ___enforce___   11. rich ___enrich___

10. close ___enclose___

Word List
1. deflate
2. demerit
3. declaw
4. derail
5. impure
6. immobile
7. imperfect
8. impolite
9. prefix
10. preview
11. preheat
12. preschool
13. costar
14. copilot
15. cohost
16. copay
17. enlarge
18. enclose
19. enrich
20. enforce

Challenge Words
21. dehydrate
22. immature
23. cooperate

Spelling (continued)

co-, together, with

12. host ___cohost___   **14.** pay ___copay___

13. pilot ___copilot___

 **Apply**   **Write the base word for each word family.**

15. larger   largest   enlarge   ___large___

16. reheat   preheat   heater   ___heat___

17. impure   purer   purest   ___pure___

18. preview   review   viewer   ___view___

19. enclose   closed   closing   ___close___

Add the prefixes de-, im-, en-, or co- to write a spelling word. The first one is done for you.

	de-,	im-,	en-,	co-	
20. host	___	___	___	___	cohost
21. polite	___	___	___	___	impolite
22. rich	___	___	___	___	enrich
23. rail	___	___	___	___	derail

Challenge

24. operate	___	___	___	___	cooperate
25. hydrate	___	___	___	___	dehydrate

Name _____   Date _____

Irregular Verb *To Be*

Focus

The verb *to be* is an **irregular verb. Irregular verbs** do not follow any pattern when they change from present tense to past tense.

Present	Past
Singular	
I **am**	I **was**
You **are**	You **were**
He, she, it **is**	He, she, it **was**
Plural	
We **are**	We **were**
You **are**	You **were**
They **are**	They **were**

Practice

Circle the correct form of the verb *to be* in parentheses.

1. I (**am**/is) excited about my new puppy!

2. Xavier and Lily (was/**were**) late for school this morning.

3. The doctor's office (**is**/are) open on Saturdays now.

4. Your sisters (**were**/was) wondering where you went!

5. Brownie, my dog, (**was**/were) my very first pet.

6. The baby bird (**was**/is) on our porch earlier today.

Apply

Read the paragraph. Correct any underlined verbs that are incorrect. Use proofreading marks to correct mistakes.

Melissa's family was moving, and everyone had ~~came~~ to her   come
going-away party. The music was so loud that no one had heard
the delivery person when he rang the doorbell with the pizza for the   *correct*
guests. Marcy, Melissa's best friend, ~~come~~ to the party after track   came
practice. Melissa told her that they had ~~sang~~ four songs already and sung
even her little brother Tony had sung "I'm a Little Teapot." Everyone   *correct*
~~come~~ into the living room to listen to him, because they thought he   came
sounded cute. Melissa's father told her that the telephone had ~~rang~~   rung
while she had been talking to Marcy.

Read the paragraph. Circle the correct verb in parentheses.

When she finished her phone call, Melissa checked to see
if everyone had (ate, (eaten)) the rest of the pizza. Someone told
her that her younger sister had (took, (taken)) the last piece while
Melissa had been on the phone. Her parents reminded her that
they had (gave, (given)) Melissa money so that she could order more
pizza. Everyone cheered, and Melissa called the pizza place and
(given, (gave)) someone her address again. After that, people ((took),
taken) a seat in the living room and watched movies until the pizza
was delivered. Many of them ((ate,) eaten) carrots while they waited.

Name _____ Date _____

Spelling Changes with Suffixes

Focus

The spelling of a base word sometimes changes when a **suffix** is attached to it.

Sometimes the consonant at the end is doubled before the suffix is added.

Example: **tap, tapped**

Sometimes the final *e* is removed before adding the *-ing* ending.

Example: **excite, exciting**

Sometimes a final *y* is changed to *i* before adding a suffix.

Example: **scary, scariest**

Sometimes the base word doesn't change at all when a suffix is added.

Example: **fast, fastest**

Practice A

Add the suffix in parentheses to the bold-faced base word. Make any necessary changes to the root word. Write the new word on the line.

1. **smile** (-ed) _____ smiled _____

2. **big** (-er) _____ bigger _____

3. **challenge** (-ing) _____ challenging _____

4. **fly** (-es) _____ flies _____

5. **snap** (-ed) _____ snapped _____

6. **whisper** (-ing) _____ whispering _____

7. **light** (-ing) _____ lighting _____

8. **scramble** (-ing) _____ scrambling _____

Practice B — Circle the word in parentheses that is spelled correctly.

9. The circus is an (exciting/exciteing) place to visit.

10. I (tried/tryed) to call my mom, but the phone was busy.

11. Beth's little brother keeps (shutting/shuting) the lid to the toy box.

12. Cassie (poundded/pounded) on the door until someone answered.

13. What are you (giveing/giving) your dad for his birthday?

14. I think that is the (loveliest/lovelyest) bouquet of flowers I've ever seen.

Apply — Add a suffix to each of the following words and write the new word in a sentence.

15. puzzle **Possible Answer** Shelli had a puzzled look on her face.

16. hot **Possible Answer** It seems to be getting hotter in this room.

17. connect **Possible Answer** I connected all the dots on the page.

18. early **Possible Answer** Jade arrived earlier than her sister.

19. glitter **Possible Answer** The diamond ring glittered in the light.

20. drop **Possible Answer** Wendel dropped the package and broke the dish inside.

Name _____ Date _____

Selection Vocabulary

Focus

pursuit (pûr • so͞ot) *n.* the act of chasing after (page 392)

drizzly (driz' • ə • lē) *adj.* lightly raining (page 392)

findings (fīn' • dingz) *n.* plural of **finding:** the result of an investigation (page 396)

overwhelm (ō' • vûr • hwelm') *v.* to overpower; to make helpless (page 396)

competitor (kəm • pe' • tə • tûr) *n.* someone selling goods or services in the same market as another person (page 397)

techniques (tek • nēks') *n.* plural of **technique:** a method (page 398)

peered (pērd) *v.* past tense of **peer:** to look closely (page 402)

environment (in • vī' • rən • mənt) *n.* surroundings (page 404)

Practice Circle the correct word that completes each sentence.

1. Aly's kitten darted after the bird in hot _____.
   a. pursuit **b.** peered **c.** techniques

2. Recycling aluminum cans helps save the _____.
   a. competitor **b.** pursuit **c.** environment

3. Lowell _____ through the hole in the fence to see what his neighbors were doing.
   a. drizzly **b.** peered **c.** pursuit

4. If we get a dog, it might _____ our poor little hamsters.
   a. peered **b.** overwhelm **c.** competitor

5. It has been _____ outside all day long.
   a. drizzly **b.** findings **c.** environment

6. The owner of the store down the street is my father's only _____.
   a. peered **b.** techniques **c.** competitor

Apply   Write *T* in the blank if the sentence for the vocabulary word is correct. Write *F* if the sentence is false. For each *F* answer, write the word that fits the definition.

7. *Techniques* are procedures.

   T _____

8. Your *findings* are your surroundings.

   F   environment

9. *Overwhelm* means "to observe something closely."

   F   peered

10. *Drizzly* means "rain is barely coming down."

   T _____

11. *Findings* are the answers you come up with when you investigate.

   T _____

12. Someone who owns the same kind of store you do is your *pursuit.*

   F   competitor

13. *Overwhelm* means "running after something."

   F   pursuit

14. If you *overwhelm* someone, you make him feel like he has no power over you.

   T _____

Name _____ **Date** _____

Classify and Categorize

> **Focus** Good readers classify items into categories as they read to help them organize information and understand what they read.
>
> **Classifying** means arranging people, places, or things into different groups or **categories.** When classifying and categorizing people, ideas, places, or things,
>
> • name the categories, or groups, for similar items.
>
> • list any items that fit the category.
>
> **Early American Colonies** ⟵ _Category_
> Massachusetts
> Rhode Island
> Maryland
>
> Some items can be put in more than one category.
>
> | **Early American Colonies** | **States of the United States** |
> |---|---|
> | Massachusetts | Massachusetts |
> | Rhode Island | Rhode Island |
> | Maryland | Maryland |

Practice A **Look through "The Case of the Gasping Garbage" and list all the items that fit the categories below.**

1. scientific equipment in Drake Doyle's lab

   Possible Answers test tubes, flasks, beakers, microscopes, telescopes, Bunsen burners

2. food and drinks Mrs. Doyle made for the scientists

   Possible Answers blueberry muffins, hot chocolate, coffee, tomato soup, grilled cheese sandwiches

Which of the following does not fit into the same category as the rest? Why doesn't it fit?

skateboard, car, truck, horse, wagon, roller blades, van

The horse doesn't fit because it doesn't have wheels.

Practice B
Name a category that best fits each of the groups of items below. Write the category in the spaces provided.

3. Bananas, grapes, apples, strawberries types of fruit

4. Baseball, basketball, golf, tennis types of sports

5. Lion tamers, clowns, flying trapeze artists, elephant trainers

types of circus performers

6. Richard Nixon, Ulysses S. Grant, Abraham Lincoln, Calvin Coolidge

names of U.S. presidents

Apply
Think about the subjects you learn in school, such as social studies and math. Choose your favorite subject and list any items that you might use for that subject, such as a compass for math and maps for geography. Write the subject and the items in the spaces below.

My favorite subject is: **Possible Answers** spelling

Items: paper, pencil, flashcards, spelling book

Name _____ **Date** _____

Using Indexes to Find Magazine Articles

Most libraries contain two indexes, *The Reader's Guide to Periodical Literature* and *Children's Magazine Guide*, to help you find up-to-date magazine articles. The indexes are published about once a month and are in the reference section of the library.

Features of Periodical Indexes

- The weeks or months when articles were published are on the front cover.

- Articles are arranged alphabetically by headings. After each article title is the following information: author's name, magazine, date of issue, and page numbers. Sometimes no author's name is listed.

- Some subject headings give cross-references to other subject headings in the guide.

Here is a sample of an index entry:

Subject	TOPIARY: *see also* Gardening	**Cross-reference**
Title	Transform Plants into Animals (includes photographs)	**Note**
Author	E. Blair. *Outdoor Art* Aug '04 p14-20	**Page**
Magazine		**Date**

SUBJECT of the magazine article. Subjects are listed in alphabetical order.

CROSS-REFERENCES indicate that more information on this subject can be found in another place in the index.

TITLE of the magazine article. Titles are listed in alphabetical order.

NOTES are added by the editor to give more information about the magazine article.

MAGAZINE in which the article appears.

DATE the magazine was published (month and year).

Page NUMBERS where the articles will be found in the magazine.

Choose a subject related to this unit. Find three articles on this subject using *The Reader's Guide to Periodical Literature* and *Children's Magazine Guide.* For each article, write the name of the magazine, the title of the article, the author of the article, and the date.

Your Subject **Possible Answer** *magnets*

Article 1

Magazine **Possible Answer** *Scholastic Science World*

Title of Article **Possible Answer** *"How Magnets Work"*

Author **Possible Answer** *John Doe*

Date of Publication **Possible Answer** *September 2004*

Article 2

Magazine **Possible Answer** *Super Science*

Title of Article **Possible Answer** *"Magnets Everywhere"*

Author **Possible Answer** *Kim Kingston*

Date of Publication **Possible Answer** *January 2005*

Article 3

Magazine **Possible Answer** *Kids Discover*

Title of Article **Possible Answer** *"Stuck on Magnets"*

Author **Possible Answer** *Bob Hutchins*

Date of Publication **Possible Answer** *June 2006*

Name _____ Date _____

Writing a Summary from Two Sources

 **Think**

Audience: Who will read your summary?

Possible Answer my classmates

Purpose: What is your reason for writing a summary?

Possible Answer I want to share something with them in a short period of time.

 **Prewriting**

Use this graphic organizer to summarize your two sources. Write the main idea and details of each source.

Possible Answers

Main Idea

Ben Franklin was a jack of all trades.

Main Idea

Ben Franklin was a great inventor.

He was a writer and printer.

He was a soldier and politician.

He was a musician and cartoonist.

He invented bifocals.

He invented the Franklin stove.

He invented the lightning rod.

_____

_____

_____

_____

_____

_____

_____

_____

Revising

Use this checklist to revise your summary.

☐ Do you focus on the main idea of the source?

☐ Do you include only the most important details?

☐ Do the rest of your sentences support the main idea?

Editing/Proofreading

Use this checklist to correct mistakes in your summary.

☐ Did you check your spelling?

☐ Are all commas placed correctly?

☐ Did you write in complete sentences?

Publishing

Use this checklist to get ready for publication.

☐ Read your summary again to make sure it is complete.

☐ Write or type a neat final copy.

Name _____ Date _____

Spelling changes with affixes

Focus
- Sometimes the spelling of a base word changes when you add a suffix. Many words change in predictable ways. Some changes are less predictable.
- If a word ends in e and the ending begins with a vowel, the e is dropped.

Practice A

Write the spelling words that end in *–or* or *-ous.*

1. cautious
2. nervous
3. furious
4. senator
5. juror
6. elevator

Challenge

7. emperor
8. ambitious

Write the spelling words that end in *-ity.*

9. activity
10. rarity
11. mobility
12. clarity

Challenge

13. curiosity

Write the spelling words that end in *–ment.*

14. argument
15. supplement

Word List
1. drizzly
2. crumbly
3. sensibly
4. terribly
5. activity
6. rarity
7. mobility
8. clarity
9. diversion
10. collision
11. tension
12. intrusion
13. argument
14. supplement
15. elevator
16. juror
17. senator
18. furious
19. nervous
20. cautious

Challenge Words
21. curiosity
22. emperor
23. ambitious

Practice B Look at these examples of spelling words and complete each statement below.

16. diverse   diversion
    tense   tension

To add *–ion* to words that end in *se*,
drop the e and add *-ion*

17. collide   collision
    intrude   intrusion

To add *–ion* to words that end in *de*,
drop *de* and add, *-sion*

Apply Write the spelling word that is related to each of these words.

18. crumb ___crumbly___

19. clear ___clarity___

20. jury ___juror___

Challenge

21. empire ___emperor___

22. curious ___curiosity___

Name _____ Date _____

Subject-Verb Agreement

Focus

Subject-verb agreement in a sentence means the verb agrees with the subject in number.

Rule

- The subject of a sentence is either singular or plural. The verb must agree with the subject in number.

- A **compound subject** that uses the conjunction *and* takes a verb that agrees with a plural subject. However, in a compound subject that uses *or*, the verb must agree with the *closest* subject word.

- With a singular subject, add *-s* or *-es* to a regular verb. With a plural subject, do not add *-s* or *-es* to the verb.

- Irregular verbs have plural forms that are quite different from their singular forms. Do not add *-s* or *-es* to these verbs to make the plural forms.

Example

- She **works** at the movie theater. We **work** at the movie theater.

- Justin and Kayla **swim** for the Hillsboro Aquasharks. Their sisters or their brother **cooks** dinner for them every night.

- Raul **eats** lunch at the diner. The teenagers **eat** lunch at the diner.

- Mrs. Kent **has** an appointment. Her daughters **have** a band concert.

Practice A

Read the paragraph. Circle the verb in parentheses that agrees with the subject of each sentence.

How (do, does) people (decide, decides) what to watch on TV? Sometimes, they (take, takes) turns or (flip, flips) a coin. Parents often (tell, tells) their children which programs (is, are) appropriate. Parents (want, wants) to make sure the television programs they choose (is, are) good for kids to watch.

Practice B Read the sentences. Change the underlined verbs to agree with the subject of each sentence. Write the correct words above the underlined words.

         are   have

1 Fossils is the remains of animals and plants that has died.

        form   are

2. Fossils forms from objects that is hard.

          look

3. Some fossils looks like dinosaur footprints.

       needs   are

4. A scientist need a microscope when the fossils is very small.

        traps   creates

5. A piece of amber trap an insect and create a fossil.

Apply Read the paragraph. Change the underlined verbs to agree with the subject of each sentence. Use proofreading marks. Write the correct words above the incorrect words.

Roxie and Madison takes swimming lessons every week.

They rides their bikes to the community center after school.

                s   s

Madison enjoy swimming the butterfly, but Roxie hate that

stroke! The girls' parents or their sisters gives them rides

                                     are

home after practice. Roxie's brother and her dog is scared of

                            es

water. They both screams if water touch them. A dog treat or

                    is

a pat on the head are a way to quiet the dog. A bowl of cereal

 es

do the trick for Roxie's brother.

Name _____   Date _____

Homographs

Focus   Do you remember the difference between **homographs** and **homophones?**

Homographs are words that are spelled the same and pronounced differently.

Example: I wiped a **tear** from my eye. Don't **tear** that page, please.

Homophones are spelled differently but pronounced the same.

Example: **Their** house is red. Look over **there!**
Today's lesson will focus on **homographs.**

Practice   Write two definitions for each homograph.

1. tear **Possible Answer** a drop of moisture from the eye; to rip

_____

2. wind **Possible Answer** moving air; turn

_____

3. dove **Possible Answer** a bird; past tense of dive

_____

4. lead **Possible Answer** a metal; to show the way

_____

Name _____ Date _____

Inflectional Endings

Focus

Inflectional endings are endings that change the tense of a verb or change a singular noun to a plural noun.

Examples: *-ed, -ing, -s*

Sometimes the consonant at the end of a word is doubled before the suffix is added.

Example: **clip, clipped**

Sometimes the final e is removed before adding the *-ing* or *-ed* ending.

Example: **scare, scaring**

Sometimes a final *y* is changed to *i* before adding a suffix.

Example: **party, parties**

Sometimes the base word doesn't change at all when a suffix is added.

Example: **ham, hams**

Practice

Add the inflectional ending in parentheses to the bold-faced word. Make any necessary changes. Write the new word on the line.

1. **breathe** (-ing) ___breathing___

2. **kite** (-s) ___kites___

3. **library** (-s) ___libraries___

4. **carry** (-ed) ___carried___

5. **step** (-ing) ___stepping___

6. **snap** (-ed) ___snapped___

Name _____ Date _____

Selection Vocabulary

Focus

eclipse (i • klips') *n.* a darkening or hiding of the sun by the moon or of the moon by Earth's shadow (page 424)

inventions (in • vent' • shənz) *n.* plural of **invention:** a thing that is made or thought of for the first time (page 424)

charted (chär' • təd) *v.* past tense of **chart:** to make a map (page 428)

forecasts (for' • casts) *n.* plural of **forecast:** a prediction about what will happen based on evidence (page 428)

charge (chärj) *n.* a load of electricity (page 429)

shocked (shokt) *v.* past tense of **shock:** to jolt by electricity (page 429)

genuine (jen' • yə • wən) *adj.* real; true (page 431)

mast (mast) *n.* a pole that holds sails (page 432)

Practice **Circle the word in parentheses that best fits each sentence.**

1. How many (eclipse/(inventions)) do you think Ben Franklin came up with altogether?

2. This battery needs a (mast/(charge)) if it is going to work.

3. Is that ((mast)/forecasts) long enough to hold that sail?

4. Mom made me come inside during the storm so I wouldn't get (eclipse/(shocked)) by lightning.

5. Miriam likes to make ((forecasts)/inventions) about the results she will get.

6. Vera and I (shocked/(charted)) the course we wanted our model airplane to take.

7. Is your necklace (charted/(genuine)) gold?

8. I had never seen an (inventions/(eclipse)) before today.

Apply   Match each word on the left to its definition on the right.

9. charted

10. charge

11. shocked

12. genuine

13. mast

14. eclipse

15. forecasts

16. inventions

a. zapped by electricity

b. part of boat the sail is attached to

c. a surge of power

d. when the moon or sun is hidden

e. not fake

f. new devices

g. planned a course

h. estimations of what will happen

Name _____ Date _____

Main Idea and Details

Focus
Writers use a **main idea** and **details** to make their point clear in a paragraph.

- The **main idea** is the most important point the writer makes. The main idea tells what the whole paragraph is about. Often a writer provides the main idea in a clear topic sentence at the beginning or the end of a paragraph.

- **Details** are bits of information in sentences that support the main idea in a paragraph.

Practice A
Find a paragraph in "How Ben Franklin Stole the Lightning" that has a clearly stated main idea. Write the page number and the main idea of the paragraph. Then list two sentences with details the writer gives to support the main idea.

Page ___422___ Main Idea: **Possible Answer** Ben was always

coming up with newfangled ways to help folks out, too.

_____

Detail: **Possible Answer** He was the guy who started the first

lending library in America.

_____

Detail: **Possible Answer** His post office was the first to deliver

mail straight to people's houses.

_____

Practice B Read the paragraph below. Underline the main idea. Then write two sentences with details that support the main idea.

Today we have vaccines for many different diseases. A vaccine is a special chemical substance that protects us against a certain disease. The substance is made of weak disease germs that cause the body to produce cells to fight off the disease. Recently scientists have developed vaccines for chicken pox and some types of flu.

Detail: **Possible Answer** A vaccine is a special chemical substance that protects us against a certain disease.

Detail: **Possible Answer** Recently scientists have developed vaccines for chicken pox and some types of flu.

Apply Write a paragraph about one of your favorite inventions. State your main idea in the first sentence. Then add sentences with details to support the main idea.

Possible Answer My favorite invention is the computer. You can do so many things with a computer. You can write papers. You can send e-mails and instant messages. You can design things. You can find out information about anything at all. You can play games. Computers are awesome.

Name _____ **Date** _____

Organizing Information into Subtopics

One way to organize information is to divide the information into subtopics. You can also use this technique as you are reading to summarize important information.

Choose a topic related to Ben Franklin or the scientific method. Fill in as much information as you can on the chart about your topic.

Possible Answers

Topic: Benjamin Franklin's Careers		
Subtopics	**Details**	**Details**
Politician/Statesman	U.S. ambassador to France	
Inventor	Lightning rod	Franklin stove
Author	*Poor Richard's Almanack*	

UNIT 4 **Lesson 4**

Why do you think a chart like this one is such a helpful way to organize information?

Possible Answer I can see everything in front of me all at one time.

Choose another topic from this unit. Find out as much information as you can about the topic and organize it using the chart below

Possible Answers

Topic: Steps of the Scientific Method		
Subtopics	**Details**	**Details**
Question	something you've noticed	something that interests you
Gather Information	search for clues	find explanations
Hypothesize	make a guess	use your observations
Test Hypothesis	plan experiment	try another hypothesis
Share Findings	publish in journal	help other scientists

Name _____ Date _____

Writing a Summary from Two Sources to Compare and Contrast

Think

Audience: Who will read your summary?

Possible Answer second graders

Purpose: What is your reason for writing a summary?

Possible Answer I want to share some information about science with younger kids.

Prewriting

Use this Venn diagram to compare and contrast the information you find on your two subjects.

Frogs
smooth,
moist skin
some teeth
live in water

Both
start as tadpoles
lay eggs in water
amphibians
carnivores

Toads
rough,
bumpy skin
no teeth
live on land

Revising   **Use this checklist to revise your summary.**

- ☐ Did you state both comparisons and contrasts?
- ☐ Is your summary well organized and easy to follow?
- ☐ Do the sentences in each paragraph support the main idea?

Editing/Proofreading   **Use this checklist to correct mistakes in your summary.**

- ☐ Are all words spelled correctly?
- ☐ Did you use correct punctuation?
- ☐ Did you capitalize proper nouns?

Publishing   **Use this checklist to get ready for publication.**

- ☐ Read your summary again to make sure it is complete.
- ☐ Write or type a neat final copy.

Name _____ Date _____

Inflectional endings

Focus

- The **inflectional endings** –ed and –ing usually tell when an action *happened,* or *is happening.*

- Sometimes the spelling of a base word changes when you add an inflectional ending. Changes in the base words usually follow familiar patterns.

- If a word ends in *e,* the *e* is dropped.

- If a word ends in *consonant-y,* the *y* becomes *i.*

- If a word ends in *short vowel-consonant,* double the *consonant.*

Practice A   Sort the spelling words into two groups.

Base word changes spelling

1. cried
2. married
3. amusing
4. tired
5. jogging
6. strummed
7. grinning
8. webbed
9. pleasing
10. dried
11. controlling
12. equipped
13. daring

Base word stays the same

14. charted
15. shocked
16. jerked
17. bowling
18. crying
19. feeling
20. willing

Challenge

21. newfangled
22. occurred
23. increasing

Word List

1. charted
2. shocked
3. jerked
4. bowling
5. cried
6. crying
7. married
8. amusing
9. tired
10. jogging
11. strummed
12. grinning
13. webbed
14. feeling
15. pleasing
16. dried
17. controlling
18. equipped
19. willing
20. daring

Challenge Words

21. newfangled
22. occurred
23. increasing

Skills Practice 2 • Spelling

Practice B Add the inflectional endings –ed and -ing to each base word.

	-ed	-ing
16. strum	strummed	strumming
17. please	pleased	pleasing
18. bowl	bowled	bowling
19. dry	dried	drying
20. control	controlled	controlling

Challenge

	-ed	-ing
21. increase	increased	increasing
22. occur	occurred	occurring

Circle the misspelled word in each sentence. Write the word correctly on the line.

23. Zack was (shoked) when he realized he had overslept. _shocked_

24. The handsome prince (marryed) Cinderella. _married_

25. A daring soldier was (equiped) for battle. _equipped_

Name _____ Date _____

Contractions

Focus

A **contraction** is a shortened form of two words. It is formed by combining two words and leaving out one or more letters. It includes an apostrophe to show where the letter or letters have been left out.

Examples:
He will = he'll
Was not = wasn't
They have = they've

Practice

1. **Write four contractions using a verb and the word "not."**

   Possible Answers didn't, couldn't, wouldn't, won't
   _____

2. **Write four contractions using a pronoun and the verb "will."**

   Possible Answers he'll, she'll, I'll, they'll
   _____

3. **Write four contractions using a pronoun and either the verb "is" or "are."**

   Possible Answers he's, she's, they're, we're

4. **Rewrite this sentence so that there are no contractions.**
   I'll check and see if they're here yet, but I'd say they probably aren't.

   I will check and see if they are here yet, but I would say
   they probably are not.

Name _____ Date _____

Compound Words

> **Focus**
> **Compound words** are made by joining two whole words. The two words do not necessarily keep the same meanings they had as individual words.
>
> In an **open compound,** the words are not combined into one word.
>
> In a **closed compound,** the two words are joined without a hyphen.

> **Practice** Solve these compound word riddles.

mailman stopwatch	greenhouse backyard	eggplant bookworm	firehouse ice box	headache headphone

1. (frozen water) + (square container) = _____ice box_____

2. (opposite of front) + (lawn) = _____backyard_____

3. (letters from post office) + (grown-up boy) = _____mailman_____

4. (color of grass) + (another word for a home) = _____greenhouse_____

5. (what a chicken lays) + (something that grows in a garden) =
_____eggplant_____

6. (body part that sits on your neck) + (used to call grandma) =
_____headphone_____

7. (opposite of go) + (used to tell time) = _____stopwatch_____

8. (something you read) + (used to catch fish) = _____bookworm_____

Word Structure • *Skills Practice 2*

Name _____ Date _____

Selection Vocabulary

Focus

major (mā' • jûr) *adj.* important (page 442)

common (ko' • mən) *adj.* happening often; familiar (page 443)

previous (prē' • vē • əs) *adj.* happening earlier (page 443)

randomly (ran' • dəm • lē) *adv.* by chance (page 443)

questionnaire (kwes' • chə • nâr') *n.* a printed list of questions used by researchers (page 445)

pace (pās) *n.* rate; speed (page 445)

publication (pu' • blə • kā' • shən) *n.* something that is printed or published (page 448)

rejected (ri • jek' • təd) *v.* past tense of **reject:** to turn down (page 448)

Practice Write the vocabulary word next to the group of words that have a similar meaning.

1. casually; pattern-less; haphazardly   randomly

2. stride; gait; speed   pace

3. survey; inquiry; examination   questionnaire

4. newspaper; magazine; book   publication

5. refused; declined; withheld   rejected

6. primary; main; key   major

7. before; earlier; past   previous

8. same; normal; usual   common

 **Write the word from the word box that matches each definition below.**

major	common	previous	randomly
questionnaire	pace	publication	rejected

9. __previous__ in the past

10. __randomly__ without a pattern

11. __publication__ putting something into print

12. __major__ very significant

13. __questionnaire__ asking people what they think

14. __common__ nothing out of the ordinary

15. __rejected__ said no

16. __pace__ how fast you are going

Name _____ Date _____

Author's Purpose

Writers have reasons for presenting a story in a certain way.

The **author's purpose** is the main reason for presenting a story or selection in a certain way. An author's purpose

- can be to *inform*, to *explain*, to *entertain*, or to *persuade*.
- affects things in the story, such as the *details*, *descriptions*, *story events*, and *dialogue*.

An author can have more than one purpose for writing.

Practice A **Look through "How Fast Do You Eat Your Ice Cream?" Identify the author's purpose for writing the story. Find two sentences that show the author's purpose. Write the page number and the sentences on the lines provided. Then, answer the questions below.**

Page: ___442___ Sentence: **Possible Answer** I didn't set out to write a

major paper.

Page: ___442___ Sentence: **Possible Answer** I decided to write an

article and send it to a medical journal and prove the judges wrong.

What is the author's purpose for writing the story?

Possible Answer to explain

_____

How successful was the author in achieving her purpose? Explain your answer.

Possible Answer She successfully explains why she wanted to do the

experiment, how she conducted it, and what her results were.

Practice B   **Writers can have more than one purpose for writing a selection. What other purpose did the author of "How Fast Do You Eat Your Ice Cream?" have?**

Possible Answer to inform

Find two sentences that show the author's secondary purpose. Write the page number and the sentences on the lines provided. Then answer the questions below.

Page: _____447_____ Sentence: **Possible Answer** I found that, overall, 20 percent, or 29 of the 145 students tested, got ice cream headaches.

Page: _____448_____ Sentence: **Possible Answer** The following is a pie chart of my results.

When authors *inform,* they give specific facts. When they *explain,* they tell how or why.

Apply   **Write a paragraph about a scientific topic of your choice. In your paragraph, include either details that inform or details that explain.**

Possible Answer

    Frogs begin their lives as tadpoles, or polliwogs. In the tadpole stage, frogs breathe with gills. They don't have legs. They have a tail similar to a fish's fin. As a tadpole matures, it slowly grows legs. It absorbs its tail into its body. The tadpole stage can be as short as a week or last several months.

_____

_____

_____

Name _____ Date _____

Asking Questions to Find Information

"How Fast Do You Eat Your Ice Cream?" includes topics such as ice cream headaches and testing hypotheses. Based on the story, fill in the chart with questions about four topics you would like to investigate. Write one question for each topic. Then find answers to your questions either by rereading the selection or by investigating the information in another source.

Questions About a Topic	Information I Found
1. **Possible Answer** Are people who suffer from migraines more likely to suffer from brain freeze?	**Possible Answer** Maya isn't sure, but one study showed that 93% of migraine sufferers also suffer from brain freeze.
2. **Possible Answer** Is there a scientific name for brain freeze?	**Possible Answer** From the Internet, I learned that it is also known as freezie or Frozen Brain Syndrome.

Questions About a Topic	Information I Found
3. **Possible Answer** What is the scientific explanation for a brain freeze?	**Possible Answer** From the encyclopedia, I learned that it can be sometimes triggered after a very cold substance comes into contact with the roof of the mouth. This activates nerves that cause blood vessels in the brain to dilate.
4. **Possible Answer** Can an ice cream headache be relieved in any way?	**Possible Answer** From the Internet, I learned that slowly sipping room temperature water might help.

Name _____ **Date** _____

Ordering Details in Descriptive Writing

Focus

When you are describing a place, thing, or even a person, you can write your description using top-to-bottom or left-to-right organization to help the reader see what you are describing.

Rule

- Place and location words help readers see where things are in your descriptions.

- For things that are mostly vertical, such as a person standing, describe them using top-to-bottom (or bottom-to-top) organization.

- For things that are mostly horizontal, such as an automobile or things in a room, describe them using left-to-right (or right-to-left) organization.

Example

- Here are some examples of place and location words.

  above   below   beside   on

  across   under   over   near

- Jared has black curly hair. His eyes are dark brown, and he has a cute button nose.

- On the left side of the room is my desk with my computer on it. Next to the desk stands a black floor lamp. On the right side of my room is a chair I throw all my clothes on.

Practice

Underline the place and location words and write which type of organization is used in the paragraph.

I rearranged the shelves so my one-year-old brother couldn't get into trouble. I put breakable things <u>on</u> the <u>top</u> shelf and unbreakable things <u>on</u> the <u>middle</u> shelf. I put the things he could play with <u>on</u> the <u>bottom</u> shelf.

What type of organization is used in this paragraph?

<u>top to bottom</u> _____

Explaining a Scientific Process

Think

Audience: Who will read your scientific process?

Possible Answer my classmates (fellow scientists)

Purpose: What is your reason for writing a scientific process?

Possible Answer I want to explain my science experiment and how I arrived at my results.

Revising **Use this checklist to revise your explanation.**

- ☐ Is each step clearly written?
- ☐ Have you left out any important steps or information?
- ☐ Did you include words that show the order of the steps?
- ☐ Did you explain why this process is important to readers?

Editing/Proofreading **Use this checklist to correct mistakes in your explanation.**

- ☐ Did you check your spelling, even if you used a computer spell-checker?
- ☐ Do all your sentences have the correct end punctuation?
- ☐ Do you use commas correctly in compound and complex sentences?

Publishing **Use this checklist to get ready for publication.**

- ☐ Read your process again to make sure it is complete.
- ☐ Include a diagram or other illustration to help readers understand the process.
- ☐ Write or type a neat final copy.

Name _____ Date _____

Compound words

Focus Compound words are words made by combining two or more smaller words.

Practice Break each compound word into two smaller words.

1. every one
2. side ways
3. lap top
4. play ground
5. bath tub
6. swim suit
7. mail box
8. gold fish
9. up stairs
10. blue berry
11. heart beat
12. tea spoon
13. pop corn
14. birth day
15. fire place
16. key board
17. year book
18. rain bow
19. wheel chair
20. town house

Challenge

21. night time
22. hand kerchief
23. quarter back

Word List
1. everyone
2. sideways
3. laptop
4. playground
5. bathtub
6. swimsuit
7. mailbox
8. goldfish
9. upstairs
10. blueberry
11. heartbeat
12. teaspoon
13. popcorn
14. birthday
15. fireplace
16. keyboard
17. yearbook
18. rainbow
19. wheelchair
20. townhouse

Challenge Words
21. nighttime
22. handkerchief
23. quarterback

Apply Use the two smaller words that make up the compound word to write the meaning of the compound word. You may use a dictionary to find the meanings of words you do not know. The first one is done for you.

24. fireplace   a place that contains fire

25. wheelchair   a chair with wheels

26. mailbox   a box for mail

27. heartbeat   the beat of a heart

28. playground   ground to play on

29. goldfish   a fish that's gold

30. birthday   the day of your birth

Challenge

31. nighttime   the time called night

32. handkerchief   a kerchief for the hand

Underline the correct spelling of each compound word.

33. everone   everywon   <u>everyone</u>

34. <u>swimsuit</u>   swimsute   swimmsuit

35. blewberry   bluebery   <u>blueberry</u>

Name _____ **Date** _____

Sentence Tenses

Focus A **present tense** verb shows an action that is currently happening

She *dances* to her favorite song.

A **past tense** verb shows an action that happened in the past.

She *danced* for hours last night.

Practice **Identify whether each sentence is present tense or past tense.**

1. Rebecca's stomach always <u>grumbles</u> when she is hungry. ___present___

2. Her brother Mark <u>laughed</u> every time he <u>heard</u> it. ___past___

3. Eliot <u>wonders</u> how his report card will look. ___present___

4. Ruth <u>did</u> her homework right before class. ___past___

5. Steven <u>read</u> all of his comics in one day. ___past___

6. Francine <u>stands</u> at the front of the line waiting to buy tickets. ___present___

Apply **Write a sentence using the present tense of to run. Then write sentence using the past tense of to run.**

7. _____

8. _____

Name _____ **Date** _____

Correcting Run-ons and Fragments

Focus

Rule	Example
• A group of words that does not express a complete thought is not a sentence, but a **fragment.**	• Harry's new puppy. Didn't eat her food.
• A sentence with no punctuation or coordinating conjunctions between two or more independent clauses is a **run-on sentence.**	• The puppy has been quiet all day Harry doesn't know if she's sick or not.
• In a **rambling sentence,** a writer strings together many thoughts. Rambling sentences often have many *ands* in them.	• Harry kept his puppy warm and he called the vet and the vet told Harry to give the dog some medicine.
• An **awkward sentence** is a sentence that does not read well.	• Harry gave the medicine to the dog and she began to get better, so Harry was very happy about that.

Practice Read the sentences. Write either *fragment* or *run-on sentence* in the blank.

1. From 1941 to 1945, Native Americans. _____fragment_____

2. These soldiers were members of the Comanche people they helped the United States protect its military secrets during

the war. _run-on sentence_

3. The Germans didn't know anything about the Comanche language hearing more words that were different confused

them even more. _run-on sentence_

Name _____ Date _____

Greek Roots

Focus

Because so many English words come from the **Greek**, knowing Greek root words will help you to decode such words.

Here are some common Greek roots and their meanings:

logy = "science of" or "study"

eco = "environment"

geo = "earth"

graph = "write"

auto = "same" or "self"

photo = "light"

port = "to carry"

path = "feeling"

mim = "to copy or imitate"

Practice Using what you know about Greek roots, write a definition for each of the following words.

Possible Answers

1. **ecology** the study of the environment

2. **geography** the study of maps, or writings about the earth

3. **autograph** a person's own signature

4. **porter** someone who carries luggage

5. **airport** a place for planes that carry people

6. **sympathy** having feelings of pity for someone

Greek Roots

Focus Here are a few more Greek roots to add to the ones you've already learned:

tech = "art" or "skillful"

nym = "name"

opt = "eye"

ortho = "straight"

cycl = "circle"

tele = "far off" or "distant"

scope = "look at"

Practice Circle the correct word in parentheses.

1. A (synonym/orthotic) is a *name* for a word that means the same as another word.

2. An (orthotist/optometrist) is an *eye* doctor.

3. A (telephoto/photographic) camera lens helps you see objects *far away*.

4. When one animal *imitates* another, the behavior is called (synonym/mimicry).

Apply Write a sentence using each of the following words. Check a dictionary if you are unsure of their meanings.
Possible Answers

5. **optic nerve** Thankfully, the doctor said there was no damage to my optic nerve.

6. **sympathize** I can sympathize with you, because I was sick.

Name _____ Date _____

Selection Vocabulary

Focus

buzzing (bu' • zing) *v.* form of **buzz:** to be very active (page 468)

ceremony (sâr' • ə • mō • ə) *n.* a formal event, usually with speech making (page 468)

transcontinental (trants' • kon' • tə • nen' • təl) *adj.* stretching from coast to coast (page 468)

laborers (lā' • bûr • ûrz) *n.* plural form of **laborer:** a worker (page 469)

assistance (ə • sis' • tənts) *n.* help (page 469)

hastily (hā' • stə • lē) *adv.* in a hurry (page 470)

locomotives (lō' • kə • mō' • tivz) *n.* plural of **locomotive:** a train engine (page 470)

thrive (thrīv) *v.* to be successful (page 471)

Practice **Circle the word in parentheses that best fits each sentence.**

1. The (laborers/locomotives) are my favorite part of the trains.

2. Aunt Suzie (hastily/thrive) grabbed her purse and ran out the door.

3. On Friday afternoons, our classroom is always (buzzing/ceremony) with activity.

4. If anyone needs (buzzing/assistance), Mrs. Green will help.

5. Elsie's grandfather is being honored at a special (ceremony/locomotives) this evening.

6. Brice hopes his family's new apple tree will (assistance/thrive) in their backyard.

Selection Vocabulary

 **Apply**   **Match each word on the left to its definition on the right.**

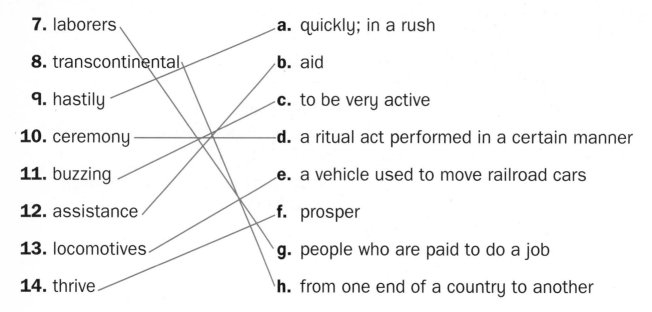

7. laborers

8. transcontinental

9. hastily

10. ceremony

11. buzzing

12. assistance

13. locomotives

14. thrive

a. quickly; in a rush

b. aid

c. to be very active

d. a ritual act performed in a certain manner

e. a vehicle used to move railroad cars

f. prosper

g. people who are paid to do a job

h. from one end of a country to another

Name _____   **Date** _____

Fact and Opinion

Focus

Writers use **facts and opinions** to support ideas in their writing.

A **fact** is a statement that can be proven true.

An **opinion** is what someone feels or believes is true.

Opinions cannot be proven true or false.

Practice A   **Look at each statement about "The Golden Spike." In the space next to each statement,** write *fact* **if the statement is a fact. Write** *opinion* **if it is an opinion.**

1. The Central Pacific line had started in San Francisco and built east.

   _____fact_____

2. Thomas Durant was the vice president of the Union Pacific.

   _____fact_____

3. The Irish workers worked harder than the Chinese workers.

   _____opinion_____

4. Leland Stanford missed his first attempt at driving in the golden spike.

   _____fact_____

5. Stanford wasn't very good at using a hammer. _____opinion_____

6. The ceremony took place in the town of Promontory, Utah.

   _____fact_____

Fact and Opinion

Practice B   Add a fact or opinion to each sentence below.
Use the clues in parentheses.

Possible Answers

7. (opinion) All cats like to ___ignore people___ .

8. (fact) All books have ___pages___ .

9. (fact) Some birds are ___smaller than my hand___ .

10. (opinion) All children are ___shorter than their parents___ .

Apply   The Golden Spike ceremony was a celebration.
Finishing a long hard job was something to celebrate.
Think of a time you celebrated something. Write two
facts and two opinions about your celebration.

Possible Answers

11. (fact) _We celebrated my grandma coming home from the_

   hospital.

12. (fact) _We had forty people in our house for the party._

   _____

13. (opinion) _It was the best celebration ever._

   _____

14. (opinion) _The food was the best anyone had ever tasted._

   _____

Name _____ Date _____

Making a List

 **Think**

Audience: Who will read your list? **Possible Answers**
the people on my research team

Purpose: What is your reason for writing a list?
I want to determine which items are
most important for us to use for our report.

 **Prewriting**

Use this graphic organizer to organize your list. Remember to arrange your items in order of importance. **Possible Answers**

Title: "Equipment needed for Promontory Ceremony"

1. several railroad ties
2. several railroad spikes
3. several sledgehammers
4. telegraph machine
5. a bullhorn or megaphone for Leland Stanford to speak through
6. the two great locomotives
7. refreshments
8. artist to paint pictures of the event
9. banners
10. list of guests

Revising   Use this checklist to revise your list.

- ☐ Is your most important item listed first, and so on?
- ☐ Does each item meet your original stated purpose?
- ☐ Would your list make complete sense to someone reading it?

Editing/Proofreading   Use this checklist to correct mistakes in your list.

- ☐ Did you check your spelling?
- ☐ Are commas and other punctuation used correctly?
- ☐ Did you capitalize proper nouns?

Publishing   Use this checklist to get ready for publication.

- ☐ Read your list again to make sure it is complete.
- ☐ Write or type a neat final copy. Add illustrations as necessary to clarify an item or items.

Name _____ Date _____

Greek Roots

Focus Many English words contain Greek roots. If you know the spellings and meanings of common Greek roots, you can figure out how to spell and define words that contain the roots.

The Greek root **arch** means "chief or first."

The Greek root **bio** means "life."

The Greek root **chron** means "time."

The Greek root **erg** means "work."

The Greek root **hydr** means "water."

The Greek root **therm** means "heat."

The Greek root **typ** means "print or model."

Word List
1. chronic
2. chronology
3. chronicle
4. biome
5. biology
6. bionic
7. biography
8. energy
9. energetic
10. hydrate
11. hydrogen
12. hydrant
13. thermal
14. thermometer
15. thermostat
16. monarch
17. architect
18. type
19. typical
20. prototype

Challenge Words
21. synchronize
22. antibiotic
23. stereotype

Practice Write all the Greek roots you recognize in these spelling words.

1. chronology __chron__ __logy__

2. biography __bio__ __graph__

3. thermometer __therm__ __meter__

Underline the Greek roots you recognize in these words.

4. bionic __bio__

5. chronic __chron__

6. energetic __erg__

7. typical __typ__

8. hydrant __hydr__

9. thermostat __therm__

10. monarch __arch__

Spelling (continued)

Write the spelling word next to its definition.

11. the first model _____ prototype _____

12. a record of events in time _____ chronicle _____

13. the study of life _____ biology _____

14. a device for measuring heat _____ thermometer _____

15. the chief designer of a structure _____ architect _____

16. the ability to do work _____ energy _____

17. an upright water pipe _____ hydrant _____

18. a written account of someone's life _____ biography _____

19. a community of life _____ biome _____

20. continuing for a long time _____ chronic _____

Name _____ Date _____

Prepositions

Focus

Rule

- A **preposition** is a word that relates a noun, pronoun, or group of words to some other word in the sentence. Prepositions usually indicate relationships of time or place.

- The noun or pronoun that follows a preposition in a sentence is called the **object of the preposition.** A preposition must have an object. It can't stand alone.

- A **prepositional phrase** is made up of a preposition, its object, and any words in between.

Example

- The cookies are **on** the third shelf.
  They are stacked **above** the crackers.

- The box of spaghetti is **beneath** the **crackers.** (*Crackers* is the object of the preposition *beneath.*)
  The sauce should be **beside** the **spaghetti.** (*Spaghetti* is the object of the preposition *beside.*)

- The food is **in the cabinet.**
  The cabinet is **near the window.**

Practice A Read the paragraph. Circle all of the prepositions.

Mongolia is a country (on) the continent (of) Asia. It is (above) China and (below) Russia. The capital city is (near) a river. Ulan Bator, the capital city, is one (of) the largest cities (in) Mongolia. There are several large cities (throughout) China and Russia. Have you ever traveled (around) China and Russia?

Prepositions

Practice B

Read the paragraph. Circle all of the prepositions. Write the word *object* above the object of the preposition.

                  object   object

Many people travel (across) North America (in) cars. The United States is

         object   object

(between) Canada and Mexico. The Rio Grande River runs (along) the American

object   object   object

border (with) Mexico, but people can still drive (to) that country. Several (of) the

      object   object   object

Great Lakes are also (near) our border (with) Canada, but visitors can drive (across)

object

them by using a bridge. Families sometimes visit Canada or Mexico (during) a

 object

vacation.

Apply

Read the paragraph. Circle all of the prepositions. Draw an *X* through each object of a preposition. Underline each prepositional phrase.

People live (in) many different areas (throughout) the United States. Some live

(with) animals (on) a farm. Others may live (in) an apartment (in) a big city. Another

group might live (near) the water, and many children live (on) quiet streets (in) small

towns. Considering the laws (of) our country. Americans can choose where they

want to live.

Name _____ Date _____

Latin Roots

Many of the English words we use today contain roots that have been borrowed from the Latin language. When you know the meaning of a Latin root, you can begin to figure out the meaning of the English word that contains it.

Here are some common Latin roots and their meanings:

rupt = "break"	*trans* = "across"
nat = "born"	*struct* = "build"
cap = "head"	*vis* = "to see"
sol = "alone"	*mar* = "sea"

Practice **Based on the meanings of the Latin roots above, write a definition for each of the following words.** Possible Answers

1. **solitude** state of being alone

2. **native** a person who was born in the country he or she lives in

3. **rupture** to break or burst

4. **captain** the head of a ship

5. **construct** to build something

6. **visible** able to be seen

7. **marina** a docking area for boats on the sea

8. **translate** to explain something across languages

Latin Roots

Focus

Here are some more common **Latin roots:**

flect or *flex* = "bend"

dent = "tooth"

cred = "believe"

anim = "life"

form = "shape"

doc = "teach"

aud = "hear"

mov, mob, mot = "move"

Practice Read the following Latin roots and their meanings. Write another word containing each Latin root beside the one provided.
Possible Answers

9. *cred* = "believe"; credible ___incredible___

10. *doc* = "teach"; doctrine ___doctor___

11. *mot* = "move"; motor ___motion___

12. *aud* = "hear"; auditorium ___audio___

Apply Write a sentence using each of the following words. **Possible Answers**

13. immobile ___Ever since my dad broke his leg, he has been immobile.___

14. reflection ___I didn't know I had ketchup on my face until I saw my reflection in the mirror.___

Name _____ **Date** _____

Selection Vocabulary

Focus

muscular (mus' • kyə • lûr) *adj.* having well-developed muscles (page 482)

generous (jen' • ər • əs) *adj.* kind and unselfish (page 482)

strain (strān) *v.* to hurt yourself by trying to do too much (page 483)

bulged (buljd) *v.* past tense of **bulge:** to swell out (page 486)

legend (le' • jənd) *n.* a story passed down through the years that is not entirely true (page 489)

versions (vûr' • zhənz) *n.* plural form of **version:** a particular telling of a story (page 489)

Practice Review the vocabulary words and definitions from "John Henry Races the Steam Drill."
Write two sentences that each use at least one of the vocabulary words.

Possible Answers

1. Mother Teresa was known for being generous to those less fortunate.

2. Raymie, Skylar, and Jen all had different versions of the fight on the playground.

Selection Vocabulary

Apply   **Fill in the blank with a vocabulary word from this lesson to complete each sentence.**

1. If you lift weights for six weeks, you'll be more ___muscular___.

2. I have heard several ___versions___ of what happened at the party.

3. When she twisted her ankle, it ___bulged___ out and began to turn blue.

4. Are you sure that story is completely true, or is it just a ___legend___?

5. Gayle's brother has always been ___generous___ with his possessions.

6. If you run hard for 45 minutes, you might ___strain___ one or more of your muscles.

Name _____ Date _____

Drawing Conclusions

Focus Drawing conclusions helps readers get more information from a story.

- **Drawing conclusions** means taking small pieces of information, or details, about a character or story event and using them to make a statement about that character or event.

- The conclusion may not be stated in the text but should be supported by details from the text.

Practice A **Look through "John Henry Races the Steam Drill" for details you can use to draw conclusions. Choose and write two different groups of details from the story and the page number. Then, write the conclusion for each.** Possible Answers

1. Page: ___480, 482___ Detail: __John Henry always sang while he drove the steel.__

   Detail: __"Before I let that steam drill beat me down, I'll die with a hammer in my hand."__

   Conclusion: __John Henry enjoyed his work.__

2. Page: ___483___ Detail: __"Don't you strain yourself, honey," said Polly Ann.__

   Detail: __John Henry smiled and kissed Polly Ann. "I ain't worried about money or clothes," he said.__

   Conclusion: __John Henry and Polly Ann loved each other more than money.__

Drawing Conclusions

Practice B Read the paragraph, and draw a conclusion.

For weeks, Marco and Allison talked about getting a pet. Marco wanted a dog for protection, but Allison felt that cats made better companions. Marco argued that a dog was the best choice, because he and Allison worked all day. The dog would bark if someone approached the house, which would help prevent a robbery. Allison felt that a cat would be a better choice, because it could be left home all day more easily than a dog. One day, Allison went shopping. When she returned home, she heard barking in the house.

Conclusion: <u>Marco went out and got a dog without telling Allison.</u>

_____

_____

Apply Write the details you used to draw your conclusion.

Detail: <u>Marco wanted a dog for protection, but Allison felt that cats made better pets.</u>

_____

Detail: <u>Allison heard barking.</u>

_____

_____

Name _____ Date _____

Observing and Recording Details

Details make explanations clear and more interesting. Details can include sensory information, such as how something looks, tastes, or sounds, that helps form pictures in the reader's mind.
When recording details, do the following:

- Jot down the important words, phrases, and ideas.

- Do not worry about spelling, punctuation, or grammar.

- Answer as many of these questions as possible: *Who? What? When? Where? Why?* and *How?*

Look at the stories in this unit about America on the Move. Think about how certain characters endured hardship, overcame obstacles, and made their mark on the history of our country. Choose a character from any of the stories. Record the details that vividly show that character's struggles or accomplishments.

Possible Answers

Character: John Henry

Details: He was the hardest-working steel-driving man of them all.

He swung his nine-pound hammer from sunup to sundown, driving a steel drill into solid rock.

He said, "Before I let that steam drill beat me down, I'll die with a hammer in my hand." The Big Bend Tunnel was hot and dusty, and the air was so foul that a man could hardly breathe.

Observing and Recording Details

Think about your investigation. Write the title of your investigation and five details you plan to include in it.
Possible Answers
My investigation title is: Title = "The California Gold Rush: The Difficult Journey by Sea"

1. Big filthy rats often ate cheese and other foods that the passengers brought with them on the ships.

2. Butter and lard wouldn't last the entire trip and spoiled, giving off a pungent, sour smell.

3. Due to a lack of fresh fruits and vegetables, many people died from scurvy (a terrible disease where your gums bleed, and there is bleeding under the skin).

4. Hundreds of people were often crammed onto one ship. It was hard to move and hard to breathe.

5. The trip was difficult for children to survive. Mostly men made the trip, leaving their families behind.

Name _____ **Date** _____

Writing a Tall Tale

 **Audience: Who** will read your tall tale? **Possible Answers**
my classmates and teacher

Purpose: What is your reason for writing a tall tale?
I want my readers to laugh and enjoy my tall tale.

 **Use the space below to plan your tall tale and practice exaggeration. Remember to use descriptive words. Possible Answers**

Character's Name: Little Clarinda McBroom

Character Traits: youngest in the family; easily upset; cries so many tears she can cause a flood

Setting: the prairie during a morning windstorm

What happens first? What happens next? When the topsoil is blown away, the McBrooms don't know how to make a living. Little Clarinda is so upset that she cries a river of salt water, which carries away the house and everyone in it. When Clarinda stops crying, the house finds land in a busy tourist spot.

How does the story end? The McBrooms make saltwater taffy from Clarinda's tears. They sell the taffy to tourists and make a fine living.

Revising Use this checklist to revise your tall tale.

☐ Do you use exaggeration?

☐ Does your plot have a beginning, a middle, and an ending?

☐ Do your characters and plot, although exaggerated, still make sense?

Editing/Proofreading Use this checklist to correct mistakes in your tall tale.

☐ Did you check your spelling?

☐ Are commas and other punctuation used correctly?

☐ Did you use quotation marks correctly?

Publishing Use this checklist to get ready for publication.

☐ Read your tall tale again to make sure it is complete.

☐ Write or type a neat final copy. Add illustrations for dramatic effect.

Name _____   **Date** _____

Latin Roots

Many English words contain **Latin roots.** If you know the spellings and meanings of common Latin roots, you can figure out how to spell and define words that contain the roots.

- The Latin root *strain* means "to draw tight"
- The Latin root *legere* means "to read."
- The Latin root *vers* means "turn."
- The Latin root *man* means "hand."
- The Latin root *rupt* means "break."
- The Latin root *sec/seq* means "following."
- The Latin root *prim* means "first or highest."

Practice Write the spelling words that contain a form of these Latin roots.

vers
1. versions
2. versus
3. adverse

strain
4. strain
5. restrain
6. constraint

Challenge
13. interrupt

legere
7. legend
8. legible
9. lecture

rupt
10. disrupt
11. abrupt
12. erupt

14. rupture

Word List
1. strain
2. restrain
3. constraint
4. legend
5. legible
6. lecture
7. versions
8. versus
9. adverse
10. manual
11. manage
12. manicure
13. disrupt
14. abrupt
15. erupt
16. secondary
17. sequel
18. sequence
19. prime
20. primate

Challenge Words
21. interrupt
22. rupture

Spelling (continued)

Apply **Meaning Strategy** Write the spelling word next to its definition.

15. to treat the hand _____ manicure

16. controlled by hand _____ manual

17. breaking off suddenly _____ abrupt

18. capable of being read _____ legible

19. to pull or draw tight _____ strain

Family Strategy The Latin roots prim and sec/seq are often associated with numbers and order. List these words as families under their roots.

prime second	secondary primary	primate primitive	sequel sequence

20. _____ prime

21. _____ primate

22. _____ primary

23. _____ primitive

24. _____ secondary

25. _____ sequel

26. _____ sequence

27. _____ second

Name _____   Date _____

Prepositional Phrases

Focus

Remember: A **preposition** relates a noun, pronoun, or group of words to another word in the sentence. *(in, through, by, with)*

The noun or pronoun that follows a preposition in a sentence is called the **object of a preposition.** (in the *house,* through the *woods,* by *her,* with *me*)

A **prepositional phrase** includes a preposition and its object. *(in the house)*

Sentences that are related can often be combined by putting some of the information into a prepositional phrase.

Example:
Many men built the railroad. John Henry was the hardest working man of them all.

New combined sentence:
Of the men who built the railroad, John Henry was the hardest working of them all.

Practice A   Circle all prepositional phrases in the following sentences.

1. Mom said she could use some help around the house after the game.

2. My friend Stella had never heard of the Washington Redskins until today.

3. Watching football is my favorite pastime in the fall.

4. I enjoy watching the players run into the stadium from the locker room.

5. Why is that player standing behind everyone else?

6. Dad said he will take me to a game for my birthday in December.

Practice B **Combine these pairs of sentences into one sentence using a prepositional phrase.**
Possible Answers

7. Mark and Zack are brothers. Zack is the older one.

Zack is the older of the two brothers.

8. I've traveled a lot of places. I liked Hawaii the best.

Of all the places I've traveled, I liked Hawaii the best.

9. I have read all of E. B. White's books. *Charlotte's Web* is my favorite.

Of all E. B. White's books, *Charlotte's Web* is my favorite.

10. Holli and Monica enjoyed tonight's performance. They liked last night's performance even better. Of the two performances, Holly and Monica enjoyed last night's better.

Apply **Rewrite each of the following sentences as two separate sentences.** **Possible Answers**

11. Of all the subjects in school, math is my favorite. We have many subjects in school. Math is my favorite subject.

12. Of the six sports at my school, football has the most participants.

There are six sports played at my school. Football is the sport that has the most participants.

Name _____ Date _____

Synonyms

Focus

Synonyms are words that have similar meanings.

Examples: *huge* and *enormous*

tiny and *little*

terrible and *awful*

poor and *penniless*

Practice A   Write a synonym for each of the following words. **Possible Answers**

1. difficult _____ hard _____

2. sleepy _____ tired _____

3. friend _____ buddy _____

4. peek _____ look _____

5. baby _____ infant _____

6. grip _____ hold _____

7. courageous _____ brave _____

8. social _____ friendly _____

9. tasty _____ delicious _____

10. yell _____ scream _____

Practice B

Match each word on the left to its synonym on the right.

11. scared
12. beautiful
13. well-behaved
14. kid
15. opportunity
16. talk
17. healthy
18. weave

a. obedient
b. chance
c. pretty
d. speak
e. child
f. braid
g. frightened
h. nutritious

Apply

Write a sentence using a synonym for each of the following words. **Possible Answers**

19. (talented) My dad is very skillful with a bow and arrow.

20. (calm) The wind died down, and the water became very still.

Name _____ Date _____

Selection Vocabulary

Focus

yearning (yûr' • ning) *v.* form of **yearn:** to long; to wish (page 498)

dreaded (dre' • dəd) *v.* past tense of **dread:** to fear (page 500)

translated (trants • lā' • təd) *v.* past tense of **translate:** to change words or thoughts from one language into another (page 500)

mainland (mān' • land') *n.* the main part of a country, as opposed to an island (page 500)

wages (wā' • jəz) *n.* plural form of **wage:** pay received for work (page 506)

strikes (strīks) *n.* plural form of **strike:** a work stoppage as a form of protest (page 506)

Practice Write *T* in the blank if the sentence for the vocabulary word is correct. Write *F* if the sentence is false. For each *F* answer, write the word that fits the definition.

1. *Yearning* means "was afraid of."

_F_ _dreaded_

2. If something is *translated,* it is changed into a different language.

_T_ _____

3. *Dreaded* means "wishing very hard and long for something."

_F_ _yearning_

4. *Wages* are when work is stopped.

_F_ _strikes_

Selection Vocabulary

Apply Circle the correct word that completes each sentence.

5. Nick _____ the geography test, because he didn't study.

    a. translated   **b.** (dreaded)   **c.** strikes

6. We took a ferry to the _____.

    a. (mainland)   **b.** wages   **c.** strikes

7. Sasha _____ her mother's words for the teacher.

    a. dreaded   **b.** (translated)   **c.** mainland

8. My _____ for my new job are much higher than for my last job.

    a. strikes   **b.** (wages)   **c.** dreaded

9. I wonder why there have been so many _____ lately at the auto plant.

    a. (strikes)   **b.** wages   **c.** yearning

10. Hermione has been _____ for a pony since she was little.

    a. translated   **b.** dreaded   **c.** (yearning)

Name _____   Date _____

Sequence

Focus

Writers use signal words to help readers understand sequence. **Sequence** is the order of events in a story.

Writers often use signal words called **time-and-order words** to show

- the passage of time in a story. Words such as *Tuesday, tomorrow,* and *the next day* show time.

- the order in which events take place. Words such as *first, then, so, when,* and *finally* show order.

Practice A   Look through "Immigrant Children." Find two sentences with time words and two sentences with order words. Write the sentences and their page numbers in the space below. Underline the time-and-order words in each sentence.

Possible Answers

1. Page: __500__ Sentence with time words: __Within a day, most families received a landing card.__

2. Page: __504__ Sentence with time words: __They washed clothes and children once a week.__

3. Page: __506__ Sentence with order words: __After that, unions got more support from the public.__

4. Page: __509__ Sentence with order words: __Next, inspections at the border grew tougher.__

Practice B | Underline the words that signal time or order in each sentence.

5. We ate lunch <u>at noon</u>.

6. <u>When the snow began</u>, we all put on our hats and gloves and ran outside.

7. <u>First</u>, he inserted the key into the lock.

8. <u>The next day</u>, we all went to the movies.

9. <u>Tomorrow</u> we will do all of our homework and be very happy.

Apply | Write a paragraph about some of the things you did recently. Use time-and-order words to indicate *when* and *in what order* you did each thing. **Possible Answers**

Last week, I visited an art museum. My mom and I got up early and picked up my cousin Sarah. Then, we drove thirty minutes to the museum. We went to see the Greek art first, because that's Sarah's favorite. Then, we went to see the photography exhibits. Mom chose Impressionistic art next. Two hours later, we had only been through half of the museum. We took a lunch break and decided to finish our tour of the museum the following day.

Name _____ **Date** _____

Interviewing

Interviewing is a way to gather information, an opinion, or a story from one person's point of view. Remember to follow these rules:

- Always ask permission to interview the person. Make sure the person knows how much time you will need for the interview.

- Make up questions that will help you get the information you need. Use questions that begin with *who, what, when, where,* or *why.*

- Write your questions in an organized order, with space after each one for taking notes.

- Speak clearly, and be polite.

- Read over your notes immediately after you leave the interview, while the conversation is still fresh in your mind.

- If you plan to record the interview with a tape recorder or a videotape recorder, ask the person's permission first.

Make a list of people you might like to interview. **Possible Answers**

my grandpa, Mrs. Sanchez, or my neighbor
_____

Write how interviews might be useful in your investigation.

Each person on my interview list is an immigrant from
another country. They might be able to help me get a
better idea of what it's like to come to a new country
and start a life.

Interviewing

Write five interview questions.   **Possible Answers**

1. When did you come to the United States?

2. With whom did you come to the United States?

3. What is the hardest thing about living in a country that is not your native home?

4. What advice do you have for other immigrants?

5. Will you ever go back to your native country to live? Why or why not?

Summarize what you learned from the interview.

Possible Answers

I learned that Mrs. Sanchez came to the United States from Mexico in 1999. She came with her husband and their three young children. It has been hard for her to learn English, but she is taking night classes at a local school. Just this past year, she got a good-paying job at a nice restaurant. She misses her parents and sisters in Mexico but visits them whenever she can. She advises other immigrants to never give up and to work as hard as they can. She may return to Mexico someday when her children are grown.

Name _____ Date _____

Writing a Book Review

Audience: Who will read your book review? **Possible Answers**
a person interested in reading the story I reviewed

Purpose: What is your reason for writing a book review?
I want to share what I liked about the story.

Use the space below to organize your book review. **Possible Answer**

Title: Henry Wells and William G. Fargo

Author: Edward F. Dolan, Jr.

Summary: Wells forms a New York-based express delivery company, and American Express, in 1842. Fargo, who worked for Wells for a while, becomes an executive at American Express. In 1852, they start a company in California, where gold is purchased from miners and then resold. They also create banks and provide other services for the gold miners.

My opinion and reason for it: I liked the story. Through hard work, both Wells and Fargo became successful businessmen.

_____

_____

Revising

Use this checklist to revise your description.

☐ Does your review have an introduction, supporting paragraphs, and a conclusion?

☐ Are your paragraphs arranged in an appropriate order?

☐ If you are reviewing a fiction book, were you careful not to give away the ending?

Editing/Proofreading

Use this checklist to correct mistakes in your description.

☐ Make sure the subjects and verbs agree in your sentences.

☐ Check all punctuation to make sure that it is correct.

☐ Make sure that all words are spelled correctly.

Publishing

Use this checklist to get ready for publication.

☐ Write or type a neat final copy.

☐ Give an oral presentation of your book review.

Name _____   Date _____

Synonyms

Focus   **Synonyms** are words that have the same, or nearly the same, meanings.

Practice   Write the spelling words that match each meaning.

felt terror

1. dreaded
2. feared

line or margin

3. border
4. edge
5. boundary
6. limit

odd or abnormal

7. weird
8. strange
9. unusual

Challenge

get or gain

10. claim
11. obtain
12. acquire

Word List
1. wages
2. salary
3. pay
4. income
5. dreaded
6. feared
7. weird
8. strange
9. unusual
10. color
11. hue
12. shade
13. problem
14. concern
15. trouble
16. crisis
17. border
18. edge
19. boundary
20. limit

Challenge Words
21. claim
22. obtain
23. acquire

Spelling (continued)

Visualization Strategy Look at each group of related words and fill in the missing letters.

13. sal__a__ry   pa__y__   __wa__ges   in__co__me

14. h__ue__   co__lor__   __sh__ade

15. tr__ou__ble   con__cern__   __cr__isis   prob__lem__

Meaning Strategy Synonyms may express different shades of meaning. For example, an event described as *weird* sounds like more than just *unusual*. Choose and write the spelling word that you think has the best shade of meaning for each blank in the story.

     Tim wanted an increase in his 16. _____, but he 17. _____ asking his boss for a raise. He had solved more than one 18. _____ for the company, and he never made any 19. _____. Tim had pushed himself to the 20. _____ and decided he just had to claim a raise.

16. __salary , wages, pay__

17. __feared, dreaded__

18. __problem, crisis__

19. __trouble__

20. __limit__

Name _____   Date _____

Sentence Combining with Appositives

> **Focus**
>
> An **appositive** is a noun that is placed next to another noun to identify it or add information about it.
>
> Reyna, my best friend, is riding to school with me today.
>
> The noun *friend* is an appositive that describes *Reyna*.
>
> An **appositive phrase** is a group of words that includes an appositive and words that describe the appositive. *(my best friend)*
>
> An appositive phrase can combine two sentences into one shorter sentence when one of the sentences provides additional information about something in the first sentence.
>
> Example: Leeza sat talking to Kiyomi. Kiyomi was a fellow immigrant.
>
> Leeza sat talking to Kiyomi, a fellow immigrant.

Practice A   **Circle the appositive phrase in each sentence. Underline the noun it describes.**

1. Papaw, (my grandfather,) takes me fishing every Saturday in the summer.

2. My cat, (Tico,) likes to chase bugs.

3. Our bus driver, (Ms. Calhoun,) is sick today.

4. Pepperoni pizza, (my favorite food,) is on the menu today.

5. Little Bill, (my neighbor,) walks his dog early in the morning.

6. I just finished reading *Boggles*, (my favorite book,) for the fifth time.

Practice B Change each of the following pairs of sentences into a single sentence, using an appositive or appositive phrase. **Possible Answers**

7. Rachel and I are going to watch *Little Women*. *Little Women* is my favorite movie.

Rachel and I are going to watch *Little Women,* my favorite movie.

8. My mom is a librarian. My mom loves books.

My mom, a librarian, loves books.

Apply Write a short paragraph about your family. At least three of the sentences in your paragraph must include an appositive phrase. **Possible Answer**

I have a pretty unusual family. There are four of us—Mom, Dad, Charlie, and me. Dad, the goofball, is always making us laugh. Mom, the best hugger in the world, is pretty funny too. Charlie, my sister, has a boy's name. It's short for Charlotte. And then there's me, the youngest. My name is Jack.

Name _____ Date _____

Antonyms

Focus

Antonyms are words that are opposite in meaning.

Examples:

beautiful and *ugly*

day and *night*

dirty and *clean*

sad and *happy*

Practice A **If the following word pairs are antonyms, write Yes. If they are *not* antonyms, write No.**

1. fat, plump ____No____

2. silly, funny ____No____

3. weak, strong ____Yes____

4. neat, messy ____Yes____

5. yes, no ____Yes____

6. interesting, boring ____Yes____

7. smooth, silky ____No____

8. thin, thick ____Yes____

Practice B Write an antonym for each of the bold-faced words. **Possible Answers**

9. late _early_
10. loose _tight_
11. truthful _dishonest_
12. win _lose_
13. give _take_
14. insignificant _important_
15. outgoing _shy_
16. open _close_
17. same _different_
18. harsh _gentle_

Apply Tedd and Todd are twins, but they are nothing alike. Everything they do is the opposite of each other. Fill in the blanks with a word of your choice. The first one is done for you.

19. Tedd is smiling. Todd is frowning.
20. Todd is quiet. Tedd is _loud_.
21. Tedd is brave. Todd is _cowardly_.
22. Todd is excited. Tedd is _bored_.

Name _____ Date _____

Selection Vocabulary

Focus

era (âr' • ə) *n.* a period of history, usually several years long (page 519)

demand (di • mand') *n.* the desire for a product or service (page 521)

desperate (des' • pə • rət) *adj.* ready to take large risks with little hope of success (page 521)

borders (bor' • dûrz) *n.* plural form of **border:** artificial line where one country or state ends and another begins (page 532)

ditches (di' • chəz) *n.* plural form of **ditch:** a long, narrow pathway cut in the earth to drain water (page 533)

locals (lö • kəlz) *n.* plural form of **local:** a person who has been living in a place for a long time, unlike newly arrived people (page 535)

Practice Write the vocabulary word next to the group of words that have a similar meaning.

1. need; want; require ___demand___

2. trenches; tunnels; paths ___ditches___

3. years; time; age ___era___

4. edges; margins; dividers ___borders___

5. hopeless; despondent; reckless ___desperate___

6. citizens; neighbors; inhabitants ___locals___

Selection Vocabulary

 **Apply** Write the word that best fits each clue below.

7. Two people who were alive at the same time in history lived in the same what? _____era_____

8. Countries have special people to defend these. What are they? _____borders_____

9. If you've lived in your town all your life, you're one of the what? _____locals_____

10. The mother bird was willing to do anything to save her babies from predators.

   What was she? _____desperate_____

11. If there aren't enough copies of a video game for everyone who wants to buy one, we say the game is in high what? _____demand_____

12. When driving a car on the road, you should try to stay out of what? _____ditches_____

Name _____ Date _____

Making Inferences

Focus

Readers make **inferences** about characters and events to understand the total picture in a story.

An **inference** is a statement about a character or event in a story. To make an inference, the reader uses

- information from the story, such as examples, facts, reasons, and descriptions.
- personal experience or knowledge, which is the individual memories and experiences you bring to the story.

Practice A

Look through "The Dust Bowl." Choose a character or a story event, and make an inference about it. Write the character's name or the story event in the spaces below. Then, write the information from the story, the page number, and personal experience or knowledge, and make an inference. **Possible Answers**

Character or story event: Dorothea Lange, photographer

Page: 534

Information from the text: Dorothea Lange captured many pitiful scenes of the time. Lange's photos caught the attention of the government.

Personal experience or knowledge: I have seen a book with her photos in it.

Inference: Lange's photography has helped people remember the migrants' suffering even today.

Practice B   Read the paragraph, and make an inference. In the spaces below, write the inference and the information and personal experience or knowledge you used to make the inference.

At home, Jeanette takes care of all her family's pets. She also walks two big dogs for Mrs. Yamamoto, her next-door neighbor. In addition to these tasks, Jeanette helps her cousin Lila herd sheep for a farmer. She doesn't yell at the sheep to make them go into the corral the way Lila does. Instead, Jeanette gently pushes them into the corral. **Possible Answers**

Inference: Jeanette cares about animals.

Information from the paragraph: Jeanette takes care of all her family's pets, walks two big dogs, and is gentle with the sheep.

Personal experience or knowledge: People who love and care for their pets usually treat all animals well.

Apply   Write a short paragraph about someone who lived through the Dust Bowl. Use sentences with information that a reader could use to make an inference about that person.   **Possible Answers**

In 1938, Mildred Ward left Oklahoma with her family. They headed toward California. They were not alone. The road was full of people just like them. People were driving old cars with their possessions piled high.

Name _____ **Date** _____

Summarizing and Organizing Information

Summarizing will help you organize information and remember what you have read. When you write a summary, look for the main ideas and important details, and use your own words to tell what happens in the story.

Select a story from Unit 5. Write the title on the line below. Summarize the story by filling in the flow chart. Write the main ideas and important details from the story in your own words. Possible Answers

Title: John Henry Races the Steam Drill

How does the story begin?
John Henry worked hard every day drilling the Big Bend Tunnel.

↓

What happens next?
One day, he accepted a challenge to beat the new steam drill.

↓

What happens after that?
He tries as hard as he can to beat the drill.

↓

How does the story end?
He dies from exhaustion.

Summarizing and Organizing Information

Choose a well-known book or movie, but do not put the title of it in the flow chart. Summarize the story on the flow chart. Then, exchange papers with a partner. Guess the title of the book or movie in your partner's flow chart.

Possible Answers

How does the story begin?

There are a bunch of girls in an orphanage being bossed around by a mean woman.

↓

What happens next?

One of the orphan girls gets chosen to go live with a billionaire.

↓

What happens after that?

She gets kidnapped by people pretending to be her real parents.

↓

How does the story end?

The rich man adopts her, and they live happily ever after.

Can you guess the title? Write it here.

Annie

Lesson 4

Antonyms

Focus	**Antonyms** are words that have opposite, or nearly opposite, meanings.

Practice Write an antonym for each of these spelling words.

1. despair — hope
2. apart — together
3. boring — thrilling
4. graceful — awkward
5. mild — fierce
6. alert — drowsy
7. solid — hollow
8. request — demand
9. lazy — active
10. locals — strangers

Challenge

11. temporary — permanent

Word List
1. demand
2. request
3. strangers
4. locals
5. fierce
6. mild
7. active
8. lazy
9. graceful
10. awkward
11. thrilling
12. boring
13. drowsy
14. alert
15. together
16. apart
17. solid
18. hollow
19. hope
20. despair

Challenge Words
21. temporary
22. permanent

Skills Practice 2 • Spelling

UNIT 5 • Lesson 4 **113**

Spelling (continued)

Proofreading Strategy Underline the misspelled word in each sentence. Write it correctly on the line.

12. The elephant is not a <u>gracful</u> animal. ___graceful___

13. We used a <u>soild</u> red tablecloth. ___solid___

14. May I <u>requist</u> a special song? ___request___

15. It filled me with <u>despare</u>. ___despair___

16. You could ask the <u>lokals</u> for directions. ___locals___

17. The long ride in the car was <u>borring</u>. ___boring___

Challenge

18. Mother used a <u>permanant</u> marker to label the box. ___permanent___

Meaning Strategy Pick your favorite pair of antonyms from the spelling list and write a sentence using both words correctly. Underline the spelling words.

19. **Answers will vary.** For example, He crushed

20. the <u>hollow</u> box with a <u>solid</u> blow.

Name _____ Date _____

Keeping Verb Tenses Consistent

Focus Verb tenses within a sentence or paragraph should be kept consistent. When different verb tenses are used, the sentence sounds awkward.

Incorrect: Jamar and Lenny *ate* their lunch and quickly *drink* their milk.

Correct: Jamar and Lenny *ate* their lunch and quickly *drank* their milk.

Practice **If the bold-faced verb in each sentence is correct, write *correct*. If it is incorrect, write the correct tense of the verb on the line provided.**

1. I watched out the window for the bus and yelled at Caitlin when I **see** it.
  saw

2. We went to the zoo and **feed** the goats. _fed_

3. Hunter **rolled** the ball to his dog, and the dog chased it. _correct_

4. I will try to be at your game to **cheered** for your team. _cheer_

5. She **copied** down her assignment every afternoon and looks over it when she gets home. _copies_

6. My pants **are** getting muddy, but I didn't care. _were_

7. Strands of hair slipped out of her ponytail and **fell** in her eyes. _correct_

8. I celebrated my birthday last week, and my grandma **flies** in from Colorado.
  flew

Varying Sentence Types

Focus
Varying the length and structure of your sentences will make your writing more enjoyable to read.

You can vary your sentences by using sentences of different lengths.

You can also vary the beginnings of your sentences, sometimes using dependent clauses at the beginning, and other times beginning with the subject and ending with a dependent clause.

Practice
The sentences in the following paragraph all sound the same. Rewrite the paragraph, and vary the sentences to add interest.

Kyle and Darnell went to the zoo. They saw many animals. They saw an animal they had never seen before. It was a baby rhino. They liked the rhino. They saw a baby kangaroo too. Darnell liked the kangaroo best. Kyle liked the tigers best. Kyle and Darnell want to go back to the zoo. They want to see the animals again. There are so many animals to see at the zoo.

Possible Answer Yesterday after school, Kyle and Darnell took a trip to the zoo. They had been to the zoo before, but they had never seen a baby rhino! It was so cute! Darnell's favorite animals were the kangaroos, but Kyle really liked the tigers. They did agree on one thing—they both want to go back to the zoo as soon as possible. There are so many animals to enjoy!

Grammar, Usage, and Mechanics • *Skills Practice 2*

Name _____ **Date** _____

Contraction

Focus

A **contraction** is a shortened form of two words. It is formed by combining two words and leaving out one or more letters. It includes an apostrophe to show where the letter or letters have been left out.

Examples:

it is = it's

you will = you'll

should not = shouldn't

Practice A

Write each of the following contractions as two words.

1. didn't ___did not___

2. we've ___we have___

3. he's ___he is *or* he has___

4. what's ___what is *or* what has___

5. won't ___will not___

6. they'd ___they would *or* they had___

7. wasn't ___was not___

8. we're ___we are___

9. can't ___can not___

10. I'd ___I had *or* I would___

Contractions

Practice B Rewrite the following sentences, changing the underlined words to a contraction.

11. <u>They have</u> been waiting in line since noon.

They've been waiting in line since noon.

12. <u>I am</u> going on vacation to Montana next week.

I'm going on vacation to Montana next week.

13. Reid and Kasey <u>have not</u> finished their homework.

Reid and Kasey haven't finished their homework.

14. <u>He will</u> let us know when our pizza is ready.

He'll let us know when our pizza is ready.

15. My uncles <u>were not</u> expecting the game to be cancelled.

My uncles weren't expecting the game to be cancelled.

16. <u>I have</u> already eaten two bananas and <u>should not</u> eat a third.

I've already eaten two bananas and shouldn't eat a third.

Apply The following contractions have been formed incorrectly. Write the correct spelling of each contraction on the lines provided.

17. he'ill _____he'll_____

18. wouldv'e _____would've_____

19. willn't _____won't_____

20. arn't _____aren't_____

Word Structure • *Skills Practice 2*

Name _____ Date _____

Selection Vocabulary

Focus

rust (rust) *v.* to have the iron parts turn reddish and scaly, then fall away (page 545)

binoculars (bə • no' • kyə • lûrz) *n.* a tool for seeing far away, made of two telescopes joined together to allow the viewer to use both eyes (page 545)

scarlet (skär' • lət) *adj.* bright red (page 545)

skim (skim) *v.* to move over lightly and swiftly (page 545)

slip (slip) *v.* to put somewhere quickly and secretly (page 546)

ashamed (ə • shəmd') *adj.* feeling shame; being upset or feeling guilty because you have done something wrong (page 449)

Practice Write the vocabulary word next to the group of words that have a similar meaning.

1. drop; fall; slump _____slip_____

2. glasses; telescope; optics _____binoculars_____

3. corrode; tarnish; stain _____rust_____

4. crimson; red; ruby _____scarlet_____

5. embarrassed; humiliated; mortified _____ashamed_____

6. scan; soar; glide _____skim_____

Selection Vocabulary

Apply Fill in the blanks below with the correct vocabulary word.

1. Celia is afraid she will _____slip_____ and fall on the ice.

2. He has to use his ____binoculars____ to look at the birds in the tree.

3. Mitzi tried to scrub the _____rust_____ off of her bike.

4. Paul turned ____scarlet____ with embarrassment.

5. Steven felt ____ashamed____ when he was caught telling a lie.

6. She planned to _____skim_____ the book again before the test.

Name _____ Date _____

Drawing Conclusions from Information

Good researchers often draw conclusions from sources to bring together the various pieces of information. To **draw a conclusion** means to pair the information given in a source with your own knowledge and reasoning powers to figure out an idea not directly stated in the source.

Find two sources related to the selection, "Pop's Bridge." Write some information from each source, and then draw some conclusions by using the two sources together. Possible Answers

Source #1 Title: Suspension Bridges—encyclopedia article

Information: I found helpful information about the spans and heights of suspension bridges around the world.

Source #2 Title: "The Golden Darling" (magazine article)

Information: When it was finished in 1937, the Golden Gate Bridge was the largest suspension bridge in the world.

Conclusions based on two sources: The Golden Gate Bridge, while a feat in its day, has been surpassed in length and height by other bridges.

Choose another topic you might use for your investigation. Select two to four sources to find information about your topic. Write your topic title, your sources, and the information you found from your sources. **Possible Answers**

Topic: **Possible Answer** Drilling Tunnels—in the Past and Today

Sources: **Possible Answer** Britannica Online, "The New Austrian Tunneling Method," "Tunnels vs. Bridges"

Write a brief summary of the information here:

Possible Answer Before tunnel-boring machines were invented, drilling and blasting were the only ways to excavate a tunnel through a mountain. The NATM was developed in the 1960s and is much safer than drilling and blasting. Sometimes bridges are a better choice than tunnels when trying to create a passage through water.

Draw conclusions using the information you found about your topic.

Possible Answer If new methods of boring tunnels hadn't been invented, there would be fewer tunnels in the world and many more tunneling accidents.

Name _____ Date _____

Writing a News Story

Think **Audience: Who** is the audience for your news story? **Possible**
people in my community   **Answers**

Purpose: What is your reason for writing a news story?
I want to tell about an interesting person in our
community.

Prewriting **Use this graphic organizer to plan the lead, the
body, and the close of your news story. Decide
how to organize the main points of the story.** **Possible Answer**

1. Write the lead paragraph here. The first sentence should answer the questions *What? When? Where? Who?* The next one or two sentences should answer the question *Why?*

► Jeremiah Potter is a familiar face in the Briar Town community. Born in 1910, he has been around the block a time or two. For the last sixty years, Jeremiah has been donating fifty percent of his income to help needy children across the state.

2. This paragraph begins the body. Write the most important details here.

► Details: Jeremiah farms 1000 acres of land.

3. Write the next most important details here.

► Sells his crop and gives half the profits to children's charities.

4. Write the least important detail here.

► He has helped over 10,000 children in need.

5. Write the closing here. End with a sentence or two that summarizes the story or includes your observations.

► It is amazing what a difference one man can make. Who knows where all those boys and girls are today? I hope they're out there making a difference in their own communities, just like Jeremiah.

Revising

Use this checklist to revise your news story.

☐ Did you tell *who, what, when, where,* and *why?*

☐ Is the lead to your news story interesting?

☐ Did you organize the background information in a logical way?

☐ Have you used specific, interesting words instead of general ones?

Editing/Proofreading

Use this checklist to correct mistakes in your news story.

☐ Are the names of the people in your story spelled correctly?

☐ Are the quotations punctuated correctly?

☐ Did you make sure sentences and proper nouns begin with capital letters?

Publishing

Use this checklist to get ready for publication.

☐ Write or type a neat final copy.

☐ Include a photograph or illustration of your subject if possible.

☐ Share your news story with others. Submit it for publication if you'd like.

Name _____   Date _____

Homographs

Focus

• **Homographs** are words that are spelled the same way, but which have different meanings, and may have different origins and pronunciations.

Example: *pro' ceeds* is a noun that refers to money obtained from a business venture *pro ceeds'* is a verb that means to continue after an interruption.

Practice

Write each of these homographs in two columns where they belong. Divide each word into syllables, and use a dictionary to see the different pronunciations.

Homographs: content, number, permit, refuse, graduate

	noun	verb	adjective
1.	con' tent		con tent'
2.	num' ber	num' ber	
3.	per mit'	per mit'	
4.	ref' use	re fuse'	

Challenge:

5.	grad' u ate	grad' u ate	

Word List

1. conduct
2. rebel
3. sewer
4. insert
5. reject
6. indent
7. combine
8. suspect
9. desert
10. tower
11. reform
12. permit
13. wind
14. recount
15. number
16. sow
17. contrast
18. moped
19. refuse
20. content

Challenge Words

21. graduate
22. proceeds
23. deliberate

Apply Spelling words are used twice in each sentence below. Write the meaning for each word. You may use a dictionary to find two meanings for each homograph.

I suspect that suspect will be convicted at his trial.

6. to think or imagine

7. someone thought to be guilty

We listened to the wind wind through the trees.

8. blowing air

9. to move and turn

I will desert our troop if we camp in the desert.

10. leave or abandon

11. dry, sandy region

The sewer accidentally dropped a needle in the sewer.

12. a person who sews

13. drain pipes

Sebastian moped because his moped was stolen.

14. sulked

15. motorized bicycle

Name _____ Date _____

Homophones

Homophones are words that have the same sound but different meanings.

Most people **write** with their **right** hand.

Knowing the meaning of a word is very important when using homophones. If you do not know the meaning of a homophone, you could use the word incorrectly.

Most people **right** with their **write** hand. (wrong)

Practice A **Complete each sentence with the correct homophone.**

sole	soul

1. A person who helps others has a kind _____soul_____.
2. The bottom part of your foot is the _____sole_____.

rain	reign

3. Water that falls from the sky is called _____rain_____.
4. The people lived in peace under the _____reign_____ of a new king.

stares	stairs

5. The bright red float got many _____stares_____ during the parade.
6. I climbed the _____stairs_____ slowly.

Practice B Complete each sentence or phrase with a homophone from the box.

tale	plain	rode	way	fare
tail	road	peace	flower	fair
plane	piece	weigh	flour	

7. Sally wore a ___plain___ dress.

8. The ___plane___ landed smoothly.

9. I had a ___piece___ of cake for dessert.

10. The police department keeps the ___peace___.

11. We use ___flour___ to bake bread.

12. Roses are my favorite type of ___flower___.

13. Our dog wags her ___tail___ when she sees us coming home.

14. The captain of the ship told us a ___tale___ about life at sea.

15. One ___way___ to paint the ceiling is to stand on a ladder.

16. How much do you ___weigh___?

17. The judges were ___fair___ in awarding prizes.

18. The cost of riding on a bus or train is called the ___fare___.

19. I ___rode___ a donkey at the zoo.

20. The ___road___ was slippery after the ice storm.

Name _____ Date _____

Selection Vocabulary

**Focus**

dawn (dôn) *n.* The time when the sun comes up (page 570)

wove (wōv) Past tense of the verb **weave:** To lace together. (page 570)

pride (prīd) *n.* A feeling of worth and importance. (page 571)

huddled (hu' dəld) Past tense of the verb **huddle:** To wrap oneself tightly. (page 575)

pounded (poun' dəd) Past tense of the verb **pound:** To beat loudly. (page 575)

trembled (trem' bəld) Past tense of the verb **tremble:** To shake. (page 575)

embarrassment (im bâr' ə smənt) *n.* A feeling of shyness or of being ashamed. (page 576)

dared (dârd) Past tense of the verb **dare:** To have the courage to do something. (page 577)

Practice **Circle the word in parentheses that best fits each sentence.**

1. I could feel the house (tremble/dawn) during the earthquake.

2. A. J. took great (embarrassment/pride) in his fine piece of artwork.

3. Esteban (wove/pounded) the colorful strands of yarn into a braid.

4. The kittens (pounded/huddled) next to each other in the cold barn.

5. Dad (tremble/pounded) on my bedroom door to make sure I was awake.

6. Nan was up at the crack of (wove/dawn) this morning.

7. When Katya fell on the steps, she felt (embarrassment/pride).

8. Vanni (pounded/dared) to pick up the little snake when no one else would.

Apply   Write *T* in the blank if the sentence for the vocabulary word is correct. Write *F* if the sentence is false. For each *F* answer, write the word that fits the definition.

1. If you *wove* something, you laced it together.

_____T_____ _____

2. If you *tremble,* you shake.

_____T_____ _____

3. *Wove* is when the sun comes up.

_____F_____ _____Dawn_____

4. *Pounded* means "wrapped oneself tightly."

_____F_____ _____huddled_____

5. A feeling of worth and importance is *embarrassment.*

_____F_____ _____pride_____

6. If she *dared* to do something, she had the courage to do it.

_____T_____ _____

7. *Pounded* means "beat loudly."

_____T_____ _____

8. A feeling of shyness or being ashamed is *pride.*

_____F_____ _____embarrassment_____

Name _____ Date _____

Exploring Online Media

The Internet has search engines you can use to find information. A search engine is used to search data for specific information by typing in a keyword. The keywords must be specific and concise to help the engine narrow its search.

You can also visit specific Internet sites to find information, such as online encyclopedias, news groups, newspapers, and magazines. Certain sites also provide links to other related sites.

Think of a topic related to "Erandi's Braids" that you would like to investigate. Write your topic on the lines provided. Brainstorm specific keywords you could type into a search engine and write them down as well.

My topic: Possible Answer a Mexican village fiesta

Keywords: Possible Answer Mexico, fiesta, life in Patzcuaro

Write the names of some magazines, newspapers, or news stations on the lines below. Search these publications' Web sites to find current information on your topic.

Possible Answer Los Angeles Times, Time, CNN, Fox News, MSNBC

Choose another topic to investigate related to the unit theme
Dollars and Sense. Write your topic and possible keywords below.
Remember, if you don't find what you're looking for at first, change
your keywords a bit or brainstorm some new ones on the same topic.

My topic: **Possible Answer** goods exported by
California to other countries

Keywords: **Possible Answer** California exports,
California economy, California's natural resources

Write the names of some magazines, newspapers, or news
stations on the lines below. Search these publications' Web sites
to find current information on your topic.

Possible Answer Los Angeles Times, Time, CNN,
Fox News, San Francisco Chronicle

Write two or three interesting facts you learned about your topic.

Possible Answer California exported 1.7 billion
dollars of manufactured goods to Australia in
2003. California exported $872 million in tree nuts
in 2000.

Sometimes your investigation will lead you to a narrower or
more interesting topic. What other topics might you choose to
investigate based on what your online search revealed?

Possible Answer California's tree nuts industry

Name _____ Date _____

Writing a Personal Narrative

Possible Answers

Think

Audience: Who will read your personal narrative?

family members or friends

Purpose: What is your reason for writing a personal narrative?

I want to share a problem I had and its resolution.

Prewriting Use this graphic organizer to plan your personal narrative.

Problem or Conflict:

Grandfather moved into our small house with us.

Actions to Solve Problem or Conflict:

I gave my bedroom to Grandfather. Now I share a bedroom with my brother.
Everyone gets up at a different time in the morning.
Everyone helps prepare dinner. Mama and Papa cook. Grandfather sets the table, and my brother and I wash the dishes.

Resolution:

Our small house is big enough for all of us to live in comfortably.

Revising
Use this checklist to revise your personal narrative.

☐ Do you explain the problem or conflict and resolution clearly?

☐ Does each paragraph contain a topic sentence with details that support it?

☐ Do you use sensory details to make your narrative interesting?

Editing/Proofreading
Use this checklist to correct mistakes.

☐ Did you check all names and places for correct spelling?

☐ Did you check all punctuation and capitalization?

☐ Read your narrative aloud and listen for grammar errors.

Publishing
Use this checklist to get ready for publication.

☐ Give your story an interesting title.

☐ Write or type a neat final copy.

Name _____ Date _____

Homophones

Focus
- Homophones are words that sound alike. They have different meanings and are spelled in different ways.
- Knowing the meanings of homophones can help us know which spelling to use when words sound alike.

Practice A Write the spelling word for each meaning below. Then, write a homophone for that spelling word.

1. someone who is invited guest
   guessed
2. a thin orange vegetable carrot
   carat
3. someone who inherits heir
   air
4. snooped or meddled pried
   pride
5. narrow beams of light rays
   raise

Challenge:

6. an open marketplace bazaar
   bizarre

Word List
1. pride
2. pried
3. rays
4. raise
5. sent
6. cent
7. scent
8. forth
9. fourth
10. air
11. heir
12. guessed
13. guest
14. toad
15. towed
16. toed
17. lessen
18. lesson
19. carat
20. carrot

Challenge Words
21. bazaar
22. bizarre

Practice B

Look for seven misspelled homophones in these sentences. Underline the misspelled words and write the words on the lines provided.

Our science teacher taught a <u>lessen</u> about measurement. We <u>guest</u> the weight of different things. He said <u>forth</u> graders should know that a <u>carrot</u> weighs about 200 milligrams. We used pennies on the balance scale, and I removed one <u>sent</u> to <u>rays</u> the other arm and make it equal. Then our teacher let Jeff weigh a small <u>towed</u> from the aquarium!

7. lesson

8. guessed

9. fourth

10. carat

11. cent

12. raise

13. toad

Apply

Choose a spelling word to complete each sentence below. Write the word in the blank.

14. We saw a pride of lions at the zoo.

15. Theresa loved the scent of her new perfume.

Name _____ Date _____

Homophones

 Remember, **homophones** are words that sound alike but have different meanings.

Knowing the meaning of a word is very important when using homophones. If you do not know the meaning of a homophone, you could use the word incorrectly.

Read the following sentence:

They're going to throw their shoes over there.

- **They're** is a contraction of *they are.*
- **Their** is a possessive pronoun and an adjective.
- **There** is an adverb meaning *at* or *in that place.*

Read the following sentence:

She plans to attend two parties too.

- **To** has many meanings—it is a preposition meaning *in the direction of;* it is part of an infinitive, as in *to drink;* and it shows the recipient of an action, as in *give it* **to** *me.*
- **Too** is an adverb meaning *also, in addition, more than enough*, or *very.*
- **Two** refers to the number *two.*

Read the following sentence:

Look at that bird—it's flying to its home!

- **It's** is a contraction of *it is.*
- **Its** is a possessive pronoun, as in *its own family.*

Practice **Write a sentence using each of the following words correctly.**

1. there ___Possible Answer There are only three strawberries in the bowl.___

2. two ___Possible Answer I ate two strawberries earlier.___

Apply **Circle the correct word in parentheses.**

3. The cat got (it's/**its**) fur stuck in the thorn bush.

4. (**There**/They're) are only three days left until spring break.

5. Do you know if (there/**they're**) planning to move before school is over?

6. The girl down the street has (too/**two**) kittens for sale.

7. Laschele came over (too/**to**) our house last night.

8. Did your parents get (there/**their**) concert tickets in the mail yet?

9. (**It's**/Its) such a beautiful day.

10. I'd like a glass of orange juice, (to/**too**).

11. I think (**it's**/its) too late to sign up for soccer.

Write a sentence using both of the boldfaced words correctly.

12. there, they're ___Possible Answer I know they're over there somewhere.___

13. too, two ___Possible Answer I have two sisters, too.___

14. their, there ___Possible Answer Their dogs are sitting over there on the steps.___

Grammar, Usage, and Mechanics • *Skills Practice 2*

Name _____ **Date** _____

Homonyms

> **Focus** **Homonyms** are words that sound the same and are spelled the same, but have different meanings.
>
> Example: bat
>
> A bat is a small furry animal that flies.
>
> A bat is a stick or club used to hit a baseball.
>
> Homonyms may be the same part of speech, or they may be completely different parts of speech.
>
> Example: play
>
> We play together after school. (verb)
>
> My class performed a play. (noun)

Practice **Write two definitions for each of the following homonyms.**

1. **watch** to look at something; a time-telling device worn on the wrist

2. **fan** a machine that cools; someone who cheers for a person or team

3. **play** a drama; to engage in an activity for fun

4. **box** to fight using punches; a square container

Apply Complete each sentence with a word from the box.

fan	play	groom	hit

1. The drama club is producing a _____ play _____.

2. We should never _____ hit _____ each other.

3. I need to _____ groom _____ my dog before the show.

4. The movie was a big _____ hit _____.

5. The _____ groom _____ was late for his wedding.

6. We turn on the _____ fan _____ when the weather gets warm.

7. We _____ play _____ baseball every weekend.

8. I'm a big _____ fan _____ of action movies.

Write two sentences using the word *fair*. Use a different meaning of the word in each sentence.

1. **Possible Answer** I took my pig to the fair and won first prize.

2. **Possible Answer** Lenny didn't think the decision was fair.

Name _____ Date _____

Selection Vocabulary

Focus

clutched (klucht) Past tense of the verb **clutch:** To hold tightly. (page 588)

longed (longd) Past tense of the verb **long:** To want very much. (page 589)

wobbled (wo' bəld) Past tense of the verb **wobble:** to shake back and forth unsteadily. (page 590)

pruned (pro͞ond) Past tense of the verb **prune:** To trim as a plant. (page 592)

confident (kon' fə dənt) *adj.* Sure of oneself. (page 593)

wearily (wēr' ə lē) *adv.* In a tired way. (page 593)

perched (pûrcht) *v.* Past tense of the verb **perch:** To sit on top of something as a bird does. (page 596)

gleefully (glē' fə lē) *adv.* With great happiness. (page 597)

Practice Write the vocabulary word next to the group of words that have a similar meaning.

1. trimmed; cut; clipped   pruned

2. certain; self-assured; sure   confident

3. exhaustedly; tiredly; faintly   wearily

4. sat; rested; stayed   perched

5. gripped; grabbed; held   clutched

6. desired; wished; wanted   longed

7. wavered; shook; quaked   wobbled

8. happily; merrily; joyfully   gleefully

Apply Match each word on the left to its definition on the right.

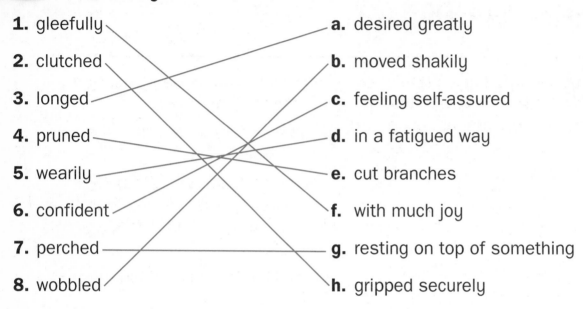

1. gleefully

2. clutched

3. longed

4. pruned

5. wearily

6. confident

7. perched

8. wobbled

a. desired greatly

b. moved shakily

c. feeling self-assured

d. in a fatigued way

e. cut branches

f. with much joy

g. resting on top of something

h. gripped securely

Name _____   Date _____

Author's Point of View

Focus

Every story is told from a specific **point of view.** Writers must decide on the point of view from which a story is told.

All stories are told through a narrator, who is the person who tells the story. The narrator can tell the story from

- the **third-person point of view.** The narrator is an outside observer and uses pronouns such as *he, she,* and *they* when telling the story.

- the **first-person point of view.** The narrator is a character in the story and uses pronouns such as *I, me,* and *my* when telling the story.

Practice

Look through the first two pages of "My Rows and Piles of Coins." Find a sentence that lets you know what point of view the author chose for the story. Write the page number, the sentence, and the point of view. Then answer the question below.

Possible Answers

Page: _____ 588 _____

Sentence: I gaped at the money until Yeyo nudged me.

Point of view: first-person

Why do you think the author chose this point of view?

to help the reader better understand the main character and feel what he's feeling

 **Read each paragraph and fill in the point of view.**

1. Mary had never eaten a cucumber in her whole life. When she saw that her plate was full of cucumber slices, she almost gave it back. Then she decided to be brave and eat this new vegetable.

   Point of view: third-person

2. Damian got a trampoline on his birthday. I got a pair of socks. Everything seems to go right for Damian, but nothing ever goes right for me.

   Point of view: first-person

3. The garden was full of weeds. It would take hours to pull out all the weeds. Gina promised to take care of the garden, but she was visiting her grandfather. There was no one around to pull the weeds—except me. So I knelt down and got to work.

   Point of view: first-person

Apply **Rewrite one of the passages above using a different point of view.**

Possible Answer I had never eaten a cucumber in my whole life. When I saw that my plate was full of cucumber slices, I almost gave it back. Then I decided to be brave and eat this new vegetable.

Name _____ Date _____

Choosing a Question to Investigate

What other questions about dollars and sense would you like to investigate?

Possible Answer Why is money so important? How can someone know the best way to use his or her money? What role has money played in our nation's history?

Now think about these questions. Where could you begin to find some answers?

Possible Answer the Internet, the library, my parents

Are there people you admire who could help you understand more about dollars and sense? Who are they? How could they help?

Possible Answer Uncle Greg: he owns his own business.

Think of two or three people you know personally and admire for their expertise with money. Write their names here.

Possible Answers my uncle Greg, my friend Terry's dad (Mr. Jackson), my mom

Choose one of these people to interview. I choose

Possible Answer my uncle Greg

Before you conduct your interview, make a list of five questions you would like to ask this person. Write them here.

Possible Answers How did you know you wanted to start your own business? What risks did you have to take? What fears did you have before you got started? What kind of research did you do? How long have you been in this business?

Write your interviewee's answers here.

Possible Answers I have been interested in money and business since I was little. I had to invest a large sum of money in my business, and that was scary because I risked failure. I researched all the other companies who were offering a similar product or service.

How will these answers help you with your investigation?

Possible Answers My uncle gave me some good tips and also shared some books and magazine articles that were helpful to him.

Inquiry • *Skills Practice 2*

Name _____ **Date** _____

Homonyms/Multiple-Meaning Words

Focus Homonyms/multiple meaning words are words that are spelled and pronounced the same way. They have different meanings and may be different parts of speech.

Practice A Say each spelling word to yourself. Then, write each word in the correct column according to its number of syllables.

1 syllable words	2 syllable words	3 syllable words
drive	batter	capital
round	figure	general
pound	reflect	
tense	anchor	
chest	minor	
pants	cooler	
point	model	
squash	counter	
	glasses	
	pupil	

Challenge:

	patient	
	measure	

Word List
1. batter
2. figure
3. drive
4. round
5. reflect
6. anchor
7. pound
8. tense
9. minor
10. cooler
11. chest
12. capital
13. model
14. pants
15. counter
16. glasses
17. point
18. general
19. pupil
20. squash

Challenge Words
21. patient
22. measure

UNIT 6 Lesson 2

Practice B

Complete each sentence with one of these spelling words. You may use a dictionary to look up different meanings for each word.

anchor	tense	glasses	point	capital

1. Bernard washed the empty _glasses_ .

2. Jerome's muscles felt _tense_ after work.

3. Start each sentence with a _capital_ letter.

4. The _point_ is sharp so be careful.

5. They raised enough _capital_ to start a business.

6. Grandmother says it is rude to _point_ at people.

7. Gloria threw the _anchor_ over the side of the boat.

8. The present _tense_ of *knew* is *know.*

9. The news _anchor_ talked about the stock market.

10. The hunters used field _glasses_ , or binoculars.

Apply

Choose one of the challenge words and use it to write two sentences that illustrate different meanings of the homonym. **Possible Answers**

11. She filled the glasses with milk.

12. He had to get glasses for reading.

148 UNIT 6 • Lesson 2

Spelling • *Skills Practice 2*

Name _____ Date _____

Sentence Combining with Appositives

Focus

An **appositive** is a noun that is placed next to another noun to identify it or add information about it.

Example: My brother, Jack, is four years old.

Jack is an appositive that describes *my brother.*

An **appositive phrase** is a group of words that includes an appositive and words that describe the appositive.

Example: Sara, Jecolia's mother, is very proud of her daughter.

Jecolia's mother is an appositive phrase that describes *Sara.*

• An appositive is usually set off by commas next to the noun it identifies.

• Appositives are *nouns.*

• Two sentences can be combined into one shorter sentence using appositives.

Example: I ate lunch with my friend. My friend is a fellow soccer player.

I ate lunch with my friend, a fellow soccer player.

Practice A

Read the following paragraph. Circle any appositives or appositive phrases you find. Underline the nouns they identify.

Tarah Rhodes, the Hollywood actress, is making an appearance in our small town today. She visited Ichabod, a neighboring town, yesterday. She has starred in over 20 movies. *Wandering,* her first movie, is one of my favorites. I hope to get her autograph and maybe a picture.

UNIT 6 Lesson 2

Practice B Appositives can make your writing more compact, make your sentences flow better, and add sentence variety. Change each of the following pairs of sentences into a single sentence, using an appositive or appositive phrase.

1. My brother is a wrestler. My brother loves to compete.

My brother, a wrestler, loves to compete.

2. I asked my mom how to do my math homework. My mom is a math whiz.

I asked my mom, the math whiz, how to do my math

homework.

3. Sally's pet goat likes to chew on people's shoestrings. Sally's pet goat is

named Chomper. Sally's pet goat, Chomper, likes to chew on

people's shoestrings.

4. I walked to the park with Tommy. Tommy is my neighbor.

I walked to the park with Tommy, my neighbor.

5. Tug asked Mrs. Wills if Tanner could play. Mrs. Wills is Tanner's mom.

Tug asked Mrs. Wills, Tanner's mom, if Tanner could play.

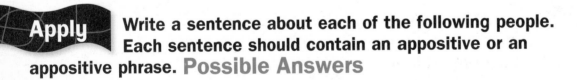

Apply Write a sentence about each of the following people. Each sentence should contain an appositive or an appositive phrase. **Possible Answers**

6. basketball coach My basketball coach, Mr. Lydell, asked us to

practice this Saturday.

7. best friend Kimmy, my best friend, lives right down the street

from me.

Grammar, Usage, and Mechanics • *Skills Practice 2*

Superlative Adjectives and Adverbs

Focus

Superlative adjectives and adverbs compare three or more things.

- Superlative adjectives compare three or more *nouns.*

- Superlative adverbs compare three or more *verbs.*

Most superlatives end in -*est.*

- Adjective: Tran is the **tallest** girl in her family.

- Adverb: Beth swims the butterfly **fastest** of any of her teammates.

Sometimes we add *most* to form the superlatives. In these cases, **do not** add -*est.*

- Adjective: The puzzle was the **most challenging** one that Lisa had ever put together.

- Adverb: Sean is the one who can type the **most skillfully** in our group.

Some adjectives and adverbs have different superlative forms.

- Adjectives with different superlative forms include *good, bad,* and *many.*

- Her grandmother's soup is the **best** in town.

- Adverbs with different superlative forms include *well, badly, much,* and *little.*

- Of all the family members, Tia plays video games the **least.**

Practice A

Read the sentences. Circle the correct superlative for each adjective.

1. Which amusement park is (biggest/most big), Splash City, Waterfest, or World of Fun?

2. World of Fun has the (scariest/most scary) roller coaster that I've ever ridden.

Practice B

Read the sentences. Circle the correct superlative for each adverb.

3. Will was the person in our group waiting (patientest/**most patiently**) for his sandwich.

4. Will and Randy performed (**best**/most well) in the talent show.

5. Tara said she'd rather see which frog could jump (**highest**/most high) in the frog jumping contest.

Apply

Read the sentences. Write the superlative form of each word in parentheses in the blank at the end of each sentence.

6. Box turtles live the (long) of any animal on our planet. _____longest_____

7. The (important) thing to remember is your raincoat. _____most important_____

8. Today is the (bad) day Tina has had all week. _____worst_____

9. Sue cheered (loudly) of anyone in the crowd. _____most loudly_____

10. Jon's baseball collection is the (big) collection in town. _____biggest_____

11. Leslie describes scenes the (well) out of anyone in our writing group.

_____best_____

Word Structure • *Skills Practice 2*

Name _____ Date _____

Selection Vocabulary

wealth (welth) *n.* A great amount of money. (page 606)

possessions (pə ze' shənz) Plural of the noun **possession**: A thing someone owns. (page 606)

protested (prə tes' təd) Past tense of the verb **protest**: To say in disagreement. (page 606)

fine (fīn) *adj.* Very nice. (page 606)

demanded (di man' dəd) Past tense of the verb **demand**: To ask firmly. (page 609)

discarded (dis kär' dəd) *adj.* Thrown away. (page 609)

Practice Review the vocabulary words and definitions from "A Spoon for Every Bite." Write two sentences that each use at least one of the vocabulary words from this lesson.

1. **Possible Answer** Our teacher demanded that we treat everyone in the class fairly.

2. **Possible Answer** We have more possessions than most people in other countries.

Apply Write the vocabulary word that fits each pair of examples.

3. said you felt the rule was unfair; objected to shutting down the animal

    shelter ___protested___

4. buying a mansion and a yacht; living in luxury ___wealth___

5. put items out for the trash; threw things away you didn't need

    ___discarded___

6. your mother told you to be kind to your sister; your father said not to cross

    the busy street ___demanded___

7. your stuffed animal collection; your new computer ___possessions___

8. a large, sparkling diamond ring; a wedding gown ___fine___

Name _____   Date _____

Compare and Contrast

Comparing and contrasting is one way to organize information in expository writing. It is sometimes useful to compare and contrast two items, such as two objects, two events, two ideas, or two people or characters. Comparing and contrasting details can help support the main idea in a piece of writing.

• When collecting or organizing information to compare and contrast, a Venn diagram is a good tool to use. Here's an example.

Cats and Dogs as Pets

Cats	Cats and Dogs	Dogs
• more independent • don't need to be walked	• fur needs grooming • daily food and water	• need a lot of attention • need to be walked

Create a Venn diagram to organize ideas for the following topic.

Compare and contrast two types of flowers or trees.

Possible Answers

Roses	Roses and Tulips	Tulips
Grow on bushes Have thorns	Come in a variety of colors Many, many species	Grow individually Grow from bulbs

Practice B

Look at each pair of words below. Write how the items in each pair are different and how they are alike.

Possible Answers

1. book   computer

   Different: Books are printed on paper and are always portable. Computers are electronic devices. Only some are portable.

   Alike: Both contain information. Both may be portable. Both may be brand-new or old and outdated.

2. babies   puppies

   Different: Babies are human. Babies are usually born one at a time. Puppies are canines.

   Alike: Both are young. Both are taken care of by adults.

Now choose one of the word pairs and compare and contrast the items in one or two paragraphs. Remember to vary your sentence structure so your writing is interesting. Possible Answers

Even though puppies are canines and babies are humans, they share a lot in common. Both are young. They have been born just recently. They are both taken care of by adults. They aren't able to care for themselves. As they get older they become more independent.

Name _____ Date _____

Using the Card or Computer Catalog

The card or computer catalog lists all the books a library has. The catalog can be found in the library's computer or on cards in a file cabinet with small drawers. Look at the sample card below.

DICK WHITTINGTON

J

398.22   Storr, Catherine.

STO   Dick Whittington/retold by Catherine Storr;

illustrated by Jane Bottomly.—Milwaukee:

Raintree Children's Books, ©1986.

[32] p.: col. ill.; 25 cm.

Summary: Retells the traditional tale of the poor boy in medieval England who became Lord Mayor of London.

1. Whittington, Richard, d. 1423

2. Folklore—England.

Here is a list of information found on cards in a card catalog.

- There are three types of cards: **author, title,** and **subject** cards. Depending on the type of card, either the author's name, the title of the book, or the subject will be at the top of the card. For instance, the title appears at the top of a title card.

- The call number is in the upper left corner of every card. This number matches the numbers and letters on the spine of the book. This number tells you where to find the book in the library.

- Every card lists the year the book was published and the name and location of the publisher, the number of pages, the abbreviation *ill.* if the book has illustrations, and the size of the book.

- The card includes a brief summary of what the book is about.

- At the bottom of each card is a list that shows all the headings the book is listed under in the card catalog.

Find two books you might use for investigation. Record the information you find in the card catalog on the blank cards below. Make sure you copy the information as it appears on the cards.

Possible Answers

J
650.12
MUR   EARNING MONEY

Murphy, Patricia J.
Minneapolis, MN: Lerner Publications, c2006.
48 p.: ill.; 23 cm.
Summary: Find out how to negotiate an allowance or start a business from kids who started their own enterprises.
Includes bibliographical references and index.

J
332.024
B452T   MONEY BOOK FOR KIDS

Berg, Adriane G.
New York: Newmarket Press, c1993, 2002.
2nd ed., xiv, 145 p.: ill.; 21 cm.
Summary: Learn how to make your money earn more money.
Additional Author: Bochner, Arthur Berg.

Name _____ Date _____

Personal Letters via E-mail

Possible Answers

 **Think** **Audience: Who** is the audience for your character's personal e-mail?

Erandi is going to write an e-mail to her cousin in America.

Purpose: What is your character's reason for writing this e-mail?

She wants to tell her about selling her braids.

 **Prewriting** **Begin drafting the body of your personal e-mail, keeping in mind your character's audience and purpose. Answer the following questions as a review of how to write a personal e-mail message.**

1. What do you type after the word "To:"?

the e-mail address of the person to whom you are sending the message

2. What is an example of a salutation?

Dear Erandi,

3. Where does the body of your e-mail start?

two lines below the salutation

4. What should you do before the beginning of each new paragraph?

indent

5. What are some words you could use for the closing of your e-mail?

Sincerely, or Your Friend

Revising
Use this checklist to revise your e-mail.

☐ Did I write everything I wanted to write?

☐ Are my tone and formality of language appropriate?

☐ Did I remember all the parts of an e-mail?

Editing/Proofreading
Use this checklist to correct mistakes in your e-mail. Use the delete and backspace keys to help you edit.

☐ Make sure that all words are spelled correctly.

☐ Check all punctuation to make sure that it is correct.

☐ Make sure sentences and proper nouns begin with capital letters.

Publishing
Use this checklist to get ready for publication.

☐ Click the word *Send* to send your e-mail.

☐ Print out a copy for yourself if you would like one.

Name _____ Date _____

Comparatives

Focus

- **Comparatives** are words that end in -er. They are adjectives that are used to compare two things
- Adding -er may require changes to the base word.
- Sometimes the y at the end of a base word changes to i before adding -er.

Practice A Remove the suffix -er and write the base word for each spelling word.

1. wealthy
2. fine
3. droopy
4. fast
5. large
6. mad
7. wide
8. lucky
9. sleek
10. sure
11. crabby
12. slim
13. warm
14. dull
15. low
16. stiff
17. little
18. firm
19. rude
20. fresh

Challenge:

21. healthy
22. tough

Word List

1. wealthier
2. finer
3. droopier
4. faster
5. larger
6. madder
7. wider
8. luckier
9. sleeker
10. surer
11. crabbier
12. slimmer
13. warmer
14. duller
15. lower
16. stiffer
17. littler
18. firmer
19. ruder
20. fresher

Challenge Words

21. healthier
22. tougher

Practice B Write the spelling word that rhymes with each of the words below. Then, use the spelling word to write a sentence that compares two things. **Answers will vary.**

1. sadder ___madder___

For example. I am even *madder* now.

2. purer ___surer___

She feels surer than those who did not study.

3. brittler ___littler___

The kitten is littler than the puppy.

4. flabbier ___crabbier___

I am crabbier in the morning.

5. grimmer ___slimmer___

Her wallet is slimmer without money.

Challenge

6. stealthier ___healthier___

She feels healthier since she started exercising.

Apply Write two spelling words that begin with the given letter. Choose words that would make sense in each sentence.

7. My dad's new car is s _____ than his old one.

___sleeker___   ___slimmer___

8. These cherries are f _____ than the ones I bought last week.

___finer___   ___fresher___   ___firmer___

9. His old bike was l _____, so it fit under the porch.

___littler___   ___lower___

Name _____ **Date** _____

Double Negatives

In English, we use only one negative word in a sentence. When two negatives occur in a sentence, we say the sentence contains a **double negative.** Some examples of negative words include *no, no one, nobody, none, not, nothing, nowhere,* and *never, aren't, won't, weren't, haven't,* and *isn't.*

Example: She **doesn't** have **no** homework to do tonight.

Corrected sentence: She **doesn't** have any homework to do tonight.

Practice A **Read the sentences. Circle the double negatives, and rewrite the sentences correctly.**

1. Tyrone says there isn't no one who will help him finish painting the house.

Tyrone says there isn't anyone who will help him finish painting the house.

2. Jake says he won't never help.

Jake says he will never help.

3. Nobody in my family can come to none of my games this month.

Nobody in my family can come to any of my games this month.

4. I don't want no cookies that have coconut in them.

I don't want any cookies that have coconut in them.

Practice B Each of the following sentences contains a double negative. On the line provided, write an affirmative word to replace the underlined word.

5. Kasey has never been to <u>no</u> baseball game. _____ a _____

6. Halley didn't do <u>nothing</u> wrong. _____ anything _____

7. Pele never got <u>no</u> ice cream. _____ any _____

8. Grandma couldn't get <u>nowhere</u> because her car is being repaired.
_____ anywhere _____

9. She <u>won't</u> tell me nothing about the soccer match. _____ will _____

10. She <u>hasn't</u> had no homework all week. _____ has _____

Apply Read the following sentences. Put an X in front of each sentence that contains a double negative.

11. _____ X _____ I hardly know nobody here.

12. _____ I can't remember the last time I saw her.

13. _____ X _____ No one told Bobby nothing about the game being cancelled.

14. _____ I couldn't have picked a better day for the garage sale.

15. _____ X _____ Mike can't eat none of that chocolate, or he'll get sick.

Name _____   Date _____

Contractions

Focus   A **contraction** is a shortened form of two words.

Examples:

does not = doesn't

can not = can't

will not = won't

should not = shouldn't

The contractions *they're, you're* and *it's* are the shortened forms of the words *they are, you are,* and *it is.* They are often confused with the possessive pronouns *their, your,* and *its. They're* is also sometimes mistaken for the word *there.*

Examples:

I know *they're* here somewhere.

Their favorite ice cream is vanilla.

What is in that big box over *there?*

Practice A   **Replace the underlined words in each sentence with a contraction.**

1. She <u>did not</u> tell me I was supposed to wear a suit. _____ didn't

2. I <u>would not</u> touch that stove if I were you. _____ wouldn't

3. I <u>can not</u> believe summer is here already. _____ can't

4. <u>It is</u> great that you can help out today. _____ It's

Practice B Read the sentences. Circle the correct word in parentheses.

5. What time does (you're, **your**) brother's plane land?

6. His friends said (their, **they're**) going to pick him up at the airport at 2:00 P.M.

7. Since (its, **it's**) almost 1:30 P.M., they should leave soon.

8. Didn't you tell me that he's bringing his guitar and all of (it's, **its**) equipment with him?

9. (**You're,** Your) going to have a famous musician visiting you!

10. No, I'm not. (Its, **It's**) just my brother.

11. I'm going to watch the singers and (**their,** they're) workers get ready for the concert.

 **Apply** Read the following sentences. If the underlined word is written incorrectly, write the correct word on the line. If the word is correct, write *Correct* on the line.

12. <u>Your</u> going to the fair tonight, right? _____ You're

13. I didn't get <u>they're</u> address before they left. _____ their

14. Brett <u>doesnt</u> have a baseball cap to wear. _____ doesn't

15. Jake said he <u>won't</u> help move the equipment. _____ Correct

Name _____ Date _____

Selection Vocabulary

Focus

daydream (dā' drēm) *v.* To let the mind wander; to think about things that may not happen (page 623)

provide (prə vīd') *v.* To give something to someone (page 623)

value (val' yoo) *n.* Worth or importance (page 625)

worthless (wûrth' ləs) *adj.* Of no use or value (page 626)

miser (mī' zûr) *n.* A person who loves money more than anything else (page 627)

misfortune (mis' for' chən) *n.* Bad luck (page 627)

Practice Write the vocabulary word that best matches the underlined word or phrase in the sentences below.

1. I often <u>let my mind wander</u> when I'm supposed to be doing homework. __daydream__

2. I feel sorry for Rachel, who has had a lot of <u>bad luck</u> lately. __misfortune__

3. My grandpa's neighbor is a grumpy <u>person who loves money more than anything else</u>. __miser__

4. This hose has a tear in it and is practically <u>of no use</u>. __worthless__

5. Your teacher will <u>give you</u> everything you need for the test. __provide__

6. The photo album might not be worth money, but it is of great <u>importance</u> to me. __value__

Apply **Write the word that best fits each clue below.**

1. Bad things have happened to you all day long. What do we call this?

misfortune

2. You give blankets and bottled water to people who have survived a hurricane.

What do you do for them? _provide_

3. You love money even more than you love people. What are you?

miser

4. Your mind wanders a lot. You imagine things that might happen someday.

What do you do? _daydream_

5. Your grandpa's antique lamp is worth a lot of money. What does it have?

value

6. Your bike tire has been punctured and can't be repaired. What is it?

worthless

UNIT 6 Lesson 4

Name _____ **Date** _____

Gathering Information

Before you begin to gather information, decide on a topic to research for your investigation.

- My group's topic:

  Possible Answer Early American pioneers and money

- Information I need to find or figure out about my topic:

  Possible Answer How early American pioneers made money, where they got the things they needed, tools they used before modern inventions

Complete the chart below to help you decide which sources will be useful.

Sources	Useful?	How?
Encyclopedias	Yes	There is a lot of information on early American pioneers.
Books	Yes	My library has an entire section of books on this topic.
Magazines	No	
Newspapers	No	
Videotapes, filmstrips, etc.	No	

Skills Practice 2 • Inquiry

UNIT 6 • Lesson 4 **169**

Drawing Conclusions from Information

Drawing conclusions from the information you find for your investigation will help you learn as you read and write. You draw conclusions by carefully reading the details and facts in the material you are reading. The conclusion may not be stated but should be supported by examples from the text.

Read the information below about sea mammals.

Whales, dolphins, manatees, seals, sea lions, and sea otters are marine mammals. Marine mammals spend most of their time underwater, but must come to the surface to breathe. Whales were once hunted for their blubber, oil, and bones. Seals and sea otters were hunted for their fur. Today, most nations have laws protecting marine mammals.

- What conclusions about marine mammals can you make after reading the paragraph? Use the information above to draw conclusions about sea mammals.

Possible Answer Marine animals are becoming endangered. If people continue to hunt these animals illegally, they could become extinct.

Name _____   **Date** _____

Pattern Poem

Think **Audience: Who** is the audience for your pattern poem?
Possible Answer my classmates
_____

Purpose: What is your reason for writing a pattern poem?
Possible Answer I want to
entertain my friends
_____

Prewriting **Use this graphic organizer to plan your poem. Use a
character or idea from one of the stories from this unit as
your topic. Place your topic in the center circle. In each
box, write descriptions or ideas that fit your topic.**

Possible Answer

Upset that someone
else might live more
lavishly

House filled with
fine furniture

Very proud of
his wealth and
possessions

The rich man
from "A Spoon for
Every Bite"

Can't sleep

Buys more and
more spoons

Revising   Use this checklist to revise your pattern poem.

- ☐ Do you create vivid images for your readers?
- ☐ Did you use rhyme and repetition?
- ☐ Do your phrases fit together and flow well?
- ☐ Is your pattern enjoyable to listen to?

Editing/Proofreading   Use this checklist to correct mistakes in your pattern poem.

- ☐ Are all words spelled correctly?
- ☐ Is all punctuation within your poem correct and consistent?
- ☐ Read your poem aloud to catch errors in rhythm and rhyme.

Publishing   Use this checklist to get ready for publication.

- ☐ Print out or write a neat final copy. Center the poem on the paper.
- ☐ Organize a poetry reading with your classmates.

Name _____   Date _____

Superlatives

Focus
- **Superlatives** are words that end in *-est*.
- They are adjectives that are used to compare more than two things.
- Adding *-est* may require changes to the base word. Sometimes the *y* at the end of a base word changes to *i* before adding *-est*.

Practice A   **Remove the suffix *-est* and write the base word for each spelling word.**

1. strict
2. wild
3. flat
4. great
5. sleepy
6. huge
7. clever
8. slow
9. sick
10. sad
11. cruel
12. kind
13. clean
14. lovely
15. wise
16. steep
17. trim
18. hungry
19. fair
20. rare

Challenge:

21. messy
22. vague
23. sassy

Word List

1. strictest
2. wildest
3. flattest
4. greatest
5. sleepiest
6. hugest
7. cleverest
8. slowest
9. sickest
10. saddest
11. cruelest
12. kindest
13. cleanest
14. loveliest
15. wisest
16. steepest
17. trimmest
18. hungriest
19. fairest
20. rarest

Challenge Words

21. messiest
22. vaguest
23. sassiest

Choose the best word to use in each sentence. Write the word on the line.

1. My big brother is the (hungry, hungrier, hungriest) person I know.

hungriest

2. It was the (sad, sadder, saddest) movie I've ever seen.

saddest

3. The (sick, sicker, sickest) patients are seen first.

sickest

4. The crow is (clever, cleverer, cleverest) than the spider.

cleverer

5. Miss Palmer is a very (fair, fairer, fairest) teacher.

fair

Challenge

6. Paint is (messy, messier, messiest) than chalk.

messier

Apply **Circle the words that are spelled correctly.**

7. (cleanest)   cleenest   clennest

8. greatist   gratest   (greatest)

9. (loveliest)   lovliest   lovelyest

10. steapest   (steepest)   steppest

Name _____ Date _____

Participial Phrases

Focus

- A **participle** is a verb form used as an adjective. Add -*ing* to a verb to form the present participle, and add -*ed* to a verb to form the past participle, unless the verb is irregular.

- A **phrase** is a group of words used as a single part of speech. It may contain a verb, but it does not contain the verb's subject.

- A **participial phrase** is a group of words that begins with a participle and modifies a noun or pronoun.

  Example: **Spinning in a circle,** LaRae lost her balance.

  Participial phrases can be used to combine two sentences, making your writing flow more smoothly.

  Example: Flo looked at her new bike. At the same time, she was grinning.

  New sentence: Grinning, Flo looked at her new bike.

Practice A **Read the following sentences and underline the participial phrase in each.**

1. <u>Cluttered with magazines and newspapers,</u> the table was not a very clean place to work.

2. <u>Looking at us carefully,</u> Claire said, "Are you sure you want to sit here?"

3. <u>Reaching for her chair,</u> she sat down slowly.

Practice B | Combine the pairs of sentences into a single sentence using a participial phrase. Write the new sentence on the line provided.

4. The baseball player was limping badly. He made it safely to first base.

Possible Answer Limping badly, the baseball player made it safely to first base.

5. My mom was filled with happiness. She welcomed my brother home from his trip.

Possible Answer Filled with happiness, my mom welcomed my brother home from his trip.

6. Our house is located in front of a forest. Our house has a nice view from our back window.

Possible Answer Located in front of a forest, our house has a nice view from our back window.

Apply | For each noun, write a sentence with a participial phrase that describes it.

7. elephant

Walking slowly, the elephant entered the water.

8. student

Wishing he had studied harder, the student began to complete his test.

9. cheerleader

Yelling loudly, the cheerleader led the crowd in a cheer.

Name _____ Date _____

Comparative Adjectives and Adverbs

> **Focus**
>
> **Comparative adjectives and adverbs** compare two things.
> - Comparative adjectives compare two *nouns.*
> - Comparative adverbs compare two *verbs.*
>
> Most comparatives end in *-er.*
> - Adjective: Tran is **taller** than her older sister.
> - Adverb: Beth swims the butterfly **faster** than her teammates.
>
> Sometimes we add *more* to form comparatives. In these cases, **do not** add *-er.*
> - Adjective: The puzzle was **more challenging** than the one Lisa received for her birthday.
> - Adverb: Sean can type **more skillfully** than the other members of our group.
>
> Some adjectives and adverbs have different comparative forms.
> - Adjectives with different comparative forms include *good, bad,* and *many.*
>   - Her grandmother's soup is **better** than the soup at the Main Street Diner.
> - Adverbs with different comparative forms include *well, badly, much,* and *little.*
>   - Tia plays video games **less** than her brother does.

> **Practice A**
>
> **Read the sentences. Circle the correct comparative for each adjective.**

1. My new puppy is (smaller/more small) than my other dog.

2. The corner deli has (better/gooder) sandwiches than the store across the street.

3. Our day at the park was (funner/more fun) than I thought it would be.

Practice B   Read the sentences. Circle the correct comparative for each adverb.

4. Candace is (carefuller/(more careful)) with her glass animals than with any other thing she owns.

5. I write fantasy scenes (badder/(worse)) than any of my friends.

6. Tom spoke (quieter/(more quietly)) in the library than he did in the hall.

Apply   Read the sentences. Write the comparative form of each word in parentheses in the blank at the end of each sentence.

7. It is (important) to brush your teeth than to watch TV. ___more important___

8. This cartoon is (funny) than the other one. ___funnier___

9. I can throw a ball (high) than my brother can. ___higher___

10. Mom's suitcase is (big) than mine. ___bigger___

11. Sarah has (little) homework tonight than she did last night.
___less___

12. Polar bears can swim (easily) in cold water than humans can.
___more easily___

Name _____ Date _____

Selection Vocabulary

Focus

opposing (ə pō' zing) *adj.* On the other side of an issue (page 637)

investment (in vest' mənt) *n.* Money someone puts into a business in order to make more money (page 637)

stencils (sten' səlz) *n.* Plural of **stencil:** a cut-out pattern used for making letter shapes with paint or markers (page 638)

partner (pärt' nûr) *n.* Someone who owns a business with another person (page 638)

profits (pro' fəts) *n.* Plural of **profit:** money a business earns (page 639)

century (sent' shə rē) *n.* A span of one hundred years (page 640)

corny (kor' nē) *adj.* Old-fashioned or sappy (page 643)

product (pro' dukt) *n.* Item that is sold by a business (page 646)

Practice Fill in each blank with a vocabulary word from this lesson to complete each sentence.

1. My mom is a ___partner___ in the law firm.

2. Gracie made a risky ___investment___, but if it works out, she'll have a lot of money.

3. Kylene used ___stencils___ to paint her name on her bedroom wall.

4. Our ___product___ is selling well, because it's something everyone can use.

5. Javier's great-grandfather has been alive for almost a ___century___.

6. I know my ideas are often ___corny___, but this one is really good.

7. __investment__ money someone puts into a business in order to make more money

8. __profits__ money a business earns

9. __product__ item that is sold by a business

10. __opposing__ on the other side of an issue

11. __stencils__ cut-out patterns used for making letter shapes with paint or markers

12. __century__ one hundred years

13. __corny__ old-fashioned or sappy

14. __partner__ someone who goes into business with others

Name _____ Date _____

Primary and Secondary Sources

Primary sources such as diaries, journals, or newspapers are useful resources for investigation. Secondary sources, or resources that offer background information on a primary source, also aid a researcher in the investigation process. In the boxes below, record examples of primary and secondary sources you have used in your investigation.

Possible Answer

Title: _Greg's Journal_   Author: _Greg Figley_

Type of primary source: _journal_

What did you learn from this resource? _I read my uncle's journal that he kept from when he started his own business two years ago._

Title: _"Local Boy Becomes Millionaire"_ Author: _Sally Star_

Type of primary source: _Newspaper_

What did you learn from this resource? _I learned how a boy in my city invented a new product and has made millions of dollars selling it across the country._

Title: ___John D. Rockefeller,___ Author: ___Ellen Greenman Coffey___
___Richest Man Ever___

Type of secondary source: ___Biography___

What did you learn from this resource? ___John D. Rockefeller had___ ___more money than anyone else of his time.___

Title: ___"Industrial Revolution"___ Author: ___no author listed (online)___

Type of secondary source: ___Encyclopedia Britannica Online___

What did you learn from this resource? ___The industrial revolution___ ___began in Britain in the late 18th century.___

Title: ___The Changemakers___ Author: ___Maury Klein___

Type of secondary source: ___Biography___

What did you learn from this resource? ___I learned how great___ ___entrepreneurs (people who start their own businesses) turn___ ___their great ideas into ways to make money.___

Name _____   Date _____

Diamante Poem

Audience: Who is the audience for your diamante poem?

Possible Answer my classmates and siblings

Purpose: What is your reason for writing a diamante poem?

Possible Answer I want to express my creativity

Use this graphic organizer to plan your poem. Write the topic of your poem at the top of the chart. Then fill in nouns, participles, and adjectives that you can use in your diamante.

Possible Answer

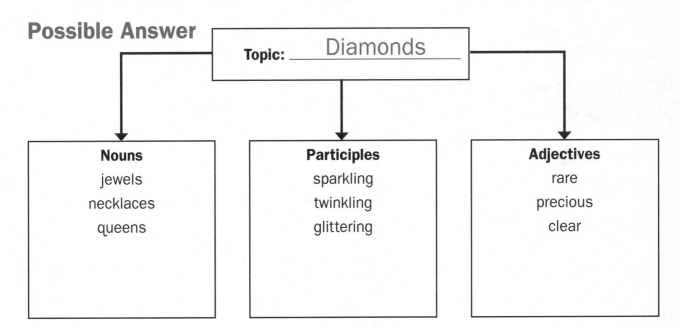

Topic: Diamonds

Nouns	Participles	Adjectives
jewels	sparkling	rare
necklaces	twinkling	precious
queens	glittering	clear

Revising   **Use this checklist to revise your diamante poem.**

☐ Did the words you chose add meaning to the poem?

☐ Did you use alliteration and assonance?

☐ Did you use several different kinds of imagery to add interest?

☐ Do your words evoke emotion?

Editing/Proofreading   **Use this checklist to correct mistakes in your diamante poem.**

☐ Are all words spelled correctly?

☐ Did you use the correct parts of speech?

☐ Read your poem aloud to detect parts that need improvement.

Publishing   **Use this checklist to get ready for publication.**

☐ Print out or write a neat final copy. Center the poem on the paper.

☐ Have your teacher display all the diamante poems on a wall or bulletin board.

Free Verse

Think

Audience: Who is the audience for your free verse poem?

Possible Answer my friends

Purpose: What is your reason for writing a free verse poem?

Possible Answer I want to entertain my friends with

an interesting poem

Prewriting

Use this graphic organizer to plan your poem. Choose an image to use as your topic. Write that topic in the center circle. Write thoughts and ideas about your topic on the lines.

Possible Answer)

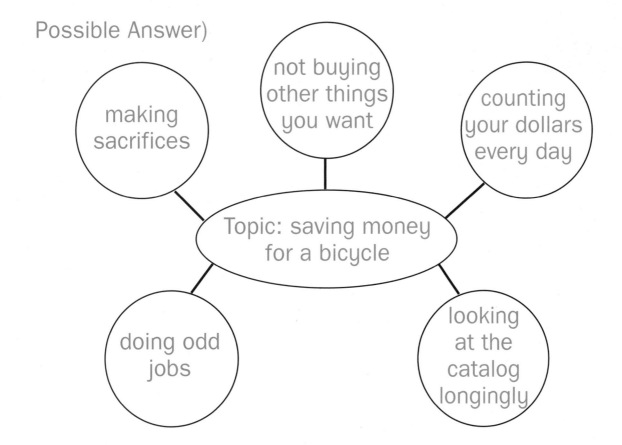

Revising   Use this checklist to revise your free-verse poem.

☐ Did the words you chose add meaning to the poem?

☐ Did you use onomatopoeic words or figurative language?

☐ Did you use several different kinds of imagery to add detail and interest?

Editing/Proofreading   Use this checklist to correct mistakes in your free-verse poem.

☐ Are all words spelled correctly?

☐ Did you use the correct punctuation?

☐ Read your poem aloud to detect parts that need improvement.

Publishing   Use this checklist to get ready for publication.

☐ Print out or write a neat final copy. Center the poem on the paper.

☐ Read your poem to the class, being sure to concentrate on diction and clarity.

Name _____ **Date** _____

Contractions

- **Contractions are shortened forms of two or more words.**
- Contractions are made by leaving out at least one letter and using an apostrophe instead.
- Some contractions are **homophones,** meaning they sound alike but are spelled differently.

Practice A Write the contraction for each pair of words

1. what is   what's
2. could not   couldn't
3. when is   when's
4. it will   it'll
5. here is   here's
6. I have   I've
7. you are   you're
8. did not   didn't
9. I had   I'd
10. let us   let's
11. she would   she'd

Challenge

12. should have   should've

Word List
1. I've
2. wouldn't
3. he's
4. you've
5. you're
6. hadn't
7. when's
8. I'd
9. couldn't
10. here's
11. didn't
12. where's
13. you'll
14. she'd
15. who's
16. they've
17. let's
18. he'd
19. it'll
20. what's

Challenge Words
21. should've
22. who'll

Practice B Some contractions are homonyms. Test each sentence below by saying the words for each contraction. Then, write the word that makes the sentence correct.

13. Jenni (here's, hears) the television downstairs.

hears

14. I suppose (he'd, heed) rather have the new one.

he'd

15. (Who's, Whose) washing the dishes tonight?

Who's

16. Where is (you're, your) coat?

your

Apply Write out the words that each of these contractions stand for.

17. they've   they have

18. who's   who is

19. where's   where is

20. he'd   he would

Challenge

21. should've   should have

22. who'll   who will,shall

Name _____ **Date** _____

Verb Tenses

Focus Verb tenses show when an action takes place in a sentence.

- A **present tense** verb shows the action is happening now. To form the present tense, add -*s* or -*es* to a regular verb that has a singular subject in a sentence. If the subject is plural, do not add -*s* or -*es* to the verb.
  Example: The horse **jumps.** The horses **jump.**

- A **past tense** verb tells about action that has already taken place. To form the past tense of a regular verb with a singular or plural subject, add -*ed* to the verb.
  Example: The horse **jumped.** The horses **jumped.**

- Some verbs don't follow rules for forming the past tense. **Irregular verbs** change their spelling for the past tense.
  Example: The jockey **rides** the horse. (present tense) The jockey **rode** the horse. (past tense)

- The **future tense** tells about an action that will happen in the future. Use the helping verb *will* in front of the base form of a verb to show the future tense.
  Example: The horse **will jump** over the water.

Practice  **Read this paragraph. Change the underlined verbs from the present tense to the past tense. Write the correct word above the incorrrect one.**

              lived   discovered
Alexander Fleming <u>live</u> from 1881 to 1955. He <u>discover</u> penicillin. In a lab
                     had   got
experiment, Dr. Fleming <u>have</u> bacteria growing in a container. Some mold <u>get</u> into
                        killed   helped
the experiment by accident and <u>kill</u> the bacteria. This discovery <u>help</u> create a

brand-new medicine.

Practice B Read the sentences. Change the words in parentheses to either the past tense or the future tense. Write the correct word above the word in parentheses.

will study
1. Jorge (study) tomorrow for the science test.

will be
2. Questions about seven famous scientists (be) on tomorrow's exam.

studied
3. Damon and Duane (study) yesterday afternoon.

told
4. Later that evening, their mother (tell) them to go upstairs to wash up for supper.

called
5. Yesterday, Jorge (call) Damon and Duane to ask them some questions about the test.

decided
6. After Jorge called, the two brothers (decide) to help Jorge.

will do
7. All three boys think they (do) well on the test tomorrrow.

Apply Read this paragraph. Change the underlined verbs to either the past tense or the future tense. Use proofreading marks to show changes. Write the correct word over the incorrect word.

was   *will*
Alexandra is sick yesterday. She take the science test tomorrow. The rest of

took
the class take it two days ago. When I go to science class today, Mr. Crawford

will   *will*   *will*   *was*
tell us when he give us our tests back. I hope that it be soon. The test is not that

studied   *did*
difficult for me, but I study for it for two hours. I wonder how the other kids do?